THE SEEDS OF HIROSHIMA

EDITA MORRIS

The Seeds of Hiroshima

MACGIBBON & KEE

FIRST PUBLISHED 1965 BY MACGIBBON & KEE LTD
COPYRIGHT © EDITA MORRIS 1965
PRINTED IN GREAT BRITAIN BY
COX & WYMAN LTD
LONDON, READING AND FAKENHAM

For Ava Helen and Linus Pauling,
Fighters for Peace and a Nobler World

'I loved your china egg. Thank you for sending it. I loved the *haiku* you wrote on it,' I tell him, for my resolutions have already broken down. As usual, I've ended by giving in to him.

And Tanso smiles. He'd so like to believe that a tender poem on a little egg will win what his ruined hands keep snatching at with desperation.

At last – off! Straddling the pillar seat, I drink in the rain as if it was saké, hanging on to my brother-in-law's belt so as not to have to put my arms around his hostile waist. In a little while I'll be seeing small sister, hearing her tinkly voice! The thought makes up for the bumps and the wind and my forced nearness to a relative whom I've come to dislike.

'How is small sister?' I ask of Hiroo's poker-straight back as we shoot through Hiroshima's rain-drenched suburbs. 'Is Ohatsu-san – well?'

No answer. Maybe he doesn't hear. (My American friend used to say that I had a voice like an insect's. Oh, Sam, Sam, your cable's burning my pocket! I'll read it again the second we've arrived.) Perhaps I'd better call a little louder.

'Hiroo . . .'

Cr-rash! Good heavens, we're in the ditch! Well, I've been expecting it ever since we tore away from Maeda's house with the rain beating in our faces. I'd have begged Hiroo to go slower, if manners hadn't forbidden such a rude request from a woman.

'Are you hurt, *nei-san*?'

9

I shake my head. The pain's so sharp that I laugh as I limp back to the motorcycle, and Hiroo sends me an approving look. Descendant of samurais, he appreciates self-control.

'Don't tell Ohatsu-san,' Hiroo orders me as he wipes off his motorcycle with a rag. 'You know how your sister worries about everything. It's very bad for her – and for the boy.'

I bow acquiescence. To be sure, small sister's baby isn't born yet, but didactic Hiroo has determined his sex. Oh, he's the limits, as Sam used to say! And yet this brother-in-law of mine is certainly – impressive. Although his trousers are baggy, although his shirt's sodden, Hiroo looks as elegant as a prince painted on silk. His hair gleams like black lacquer in the rain. He might have stepped right out of the 'Tale of Genjii'!

'You've dropped something, *nei-san*.'

I turn my head and, oh dear! There's the white slip lying in the ditch. I stoop down quickly – but it's Hiroo who picks up Sam's crumbled cable. His face is so expressionless as he hands it to me that it's obvious he suspects the worst. How is it that this Hiroo is such a stickler for convention? It shocks him that a widowed girl should receive a message from a gentleman – a young foreigner at that.

We're off again. No doubt I look dashingly modern, straddling the back of a motorcycle, my hair streaming out behind. A real '*après-guerre* girl', the onlookers must think – if there were any onlookers beside the sea-gulls shrieking in the wind.

So we're close to the Inland Sea! Yes, more gulls, diving for fish. And here's the suicide cliff of Osima, shivering inside its shawl of rain drops. Is it already years since we passed here on the train, small sister and I? (To think that people come here to throw themselves off! She had giggled, her little nose pressed against the pane. 'How could anyone be so silly?')

Our cycle slows down, halts beside a line of cypresses. The Shimitzus' antiquated house seems to be bending sideways beneath the whining trees. It hasn't known repairs for years. Its roof is sagging, its colours are faded – and yet I delight in it. Doesn't it shelter the person I love most in the world?

'Small sister!'

My – Ohatsu! I lower my eyes in order not to betray my too-great affection. My sister's beautiful face always dazzles me, like lightning in the sky. I never gaze at it for more than a second at a time.

'Come quickly!' she cries, and is motioning me to follow her. 'We have something to show you, *nei-san*. Something – wonderful!' Ohatsu giggles in her little-girl's way.

But then all at once she forgets me entirely. Hiroo has come in, and those two look at each other like lovers who have been separated for years, not hours. As she helps her husband off with his shoes, Ohatsu puts into her gesture all the adoration that manners forbid us women from expressing in words.

'You got wet, *anata*,' she whispers, her voice trembling with concern.

'Well – and the surprise?' I interrupt, then hope that my sister hasn't heard the animosity in my voice. (Oh, it's unseemly, I know, yet I can't get over my resentment with Hiroo for making this frail sister of mine bear a child.)

'Yes, come, come!' Ohatsu's all excited again. 'Oh, *nei-san* you could never guess . . .'

Small sister hastens through the adjoining room so impulsively that she forgets to salute the *hotoke* on the illuminated family altar. Contritely she retraces her steps and after arranging the folds of her kimono, bows low to the framed photograph on the shelf, lowest of all to that of Hiroo's dead father, the last in the row. Her expression is as solemn as it becomes jubilant while hurrying me into the next room, her hand on my arm.

'There, *nei-san*!'

Mà! I halt before Hiroo's easel, my hands groping for each other. My brother-in-law's modernistic pictures are dry and precise as a rule, but this self-portrait of himself with Ohatsu's child in his arms – *lives* on the canvas. As small sister and I study her husband's work, a tear rolls into my mouth. But Ohatsu laughs her tinkly laugh.

'Hiroo didn't *dare* paint baby-san's face, that's why it's hidden in shadow. Our baby will be *too* beautiful, elder sister. It would be wrong to do a likeness of him now. Later, after he's born, my husband might make another painting . . .'

Kneeling on the *tatami*, we sink ourselves into portrait-viewing. In the face of the man gazing down at his perfect offspring seems to be expressed for all time the joy of fatherhood.

'Yuka-san! *Irashai mashita. Doʐo.*'

There's a shuffling sound behind us. I rise from my knees as Hiroo's mother glides into the room with that old-fashioned gait which irreverent Sam used to refer to as 'pigeon-toeing'. We bow to each other many times, while she murmurs the pleasant phrases of welcome, smiling at me as though each one were composed especially for the occasion. My sister's mother-in-law belongs to an age when politeness vied with kindness in making a guest feel welcome.

'Please come to supper. *Doʐo,*' the old lady lisps. She moves into the next room, fluttering a snuff-coloured fan as ancient as herself. 'A very modest supper, honoured guest. Very modest,' mumbles Hiroo's mother before bowing, in her turn, to the photographs on the lacquered altar.

Oh, how proud she must feel to have given a boy as talented as her painter son to her dead husband and his fellow-*hotoke*! For a family like the Shimitzus, marriage can have no other meaning than to continue the succession. Small sister's turn now!

As we kneel around the low eating table, I keep

glancing at Ohatsu who carries within her childish body the future heir. How delicate she is, how lovely! But Ohatsu isn't conscious of my gaze. Her whole being is concentrated on Hiroo.

'A little saké, *anata*?' she asks him. And her voice quivers.

2

How soft, my *futon*! Everything's soft, everything's gentle, in this ancient house beneath the cypresses. I've snuggled down and lie rubbing my cheek against the worn brown cover. Strange! Yes, strange that small sister, years younger than me, should like to gaze at those subdued shades and listen to the whispering sounds that are the voices of her new home. (There's the rustle of a mouse in the wall, the creaking of a bough beyond the *shojii*.) Do muted colours and sounds satisfy some deep craving in Ohatsu? Do they soothe my sister, whose ears and eyes were assailed too early by the flash-bang of the *pikadon*? I turn over on my side. At once two floor-boards beneath the *tatami* set up a senile conversation.

'We are old,' they tell each other. 'We're worn, we're very old. We will last for ever.'

Come on, sleep! No, it's no use – no use. Sleep shuns lonely people, seeks loving couples lying warm in each other's arms. I try to read by the light of the candle, but I'm too tired. Keeping house for Maeda and coping with his art students is no easy work. As I lie looking at the sea-green Satsuma vase and the lacquered screen illuminated by the starlight, I can think only of my own Satsuma vase that was turned to dust and whirled away in the holocaust. I remember *my* lacquered screen, sold to raise money after Fumio's death. Twice the atom bomb tore my existence to shreds.

It's hours before drowsiness creeps over me and I feel my limbs grow heavy. I shut out all thoughts, *willing* sleep to arrive before dawn, when I must hurry back to town to get my son and daughter off to school. Ah, now sleep is here . . . now . . .

'Fumio!'

I've screamed myself awake. In my sleep my hand had reached out and searched about for my mate's. No Fumio! No hand! No husband! I lie there trembling. Oh, I can stand it no longer. No woman can endure an empty bed – an empty body . . .

'Elder sister!'

Thank heaven! Hot and alive, Ohatsu has come running in to chase away the ghosts. In the light of the stars I can make out her long shadowy form in her night kimono.

'Ohatsu-san!'

Ah, I know I shouldn't have called out. I should have pretended sleep. But I'm so lonely!

'I dreamed of – Fumio. I saw him lying in that hospital ward . . .'

'No! Oh, no!'

Ohatsu backs away from me. Seeing her frightened eyes, I am filled with shame. Haven't I yet learned how my sister dreads to be reminded of those horrors fami-

16

liar to all of us Hiroshimans? She has built a safety-wall between herself and her memories. She was only two on the day of the *gembaku*, yet the stink of burnt flesh, the sound of screams, has lingered in her mind.

'Forgive me,' I murmur and lay my cheek against my pillow, filled with rice.

'You must try and sleep, *nei-san*,' Ohatsu tells me. She's recovered herself and moves towards my *futon* in her white flowing kimono. Her long hair falls over her shoulder and arm as she peers down at me. 'I'll tell you what – I'll fetch my spirit lamp and brew you some tea. Herb tea will make you drowsy, elder sister.'

I nod gratefully and Ohatsu trots off to find her spirit lamp and matches – just like a schoolgirl preparing a secret party in the middle of the night. Against the background of the *fusuma* I can see her delicate figure and the bulge of pregnancy which, as always, seems somehow inappropriate. I try to suppress the old thought that it's all wrong for Ohatsu to have a baby. Isn't she too frail, too nervous for the ordeal? And I remember how before her marriage I made her *promise* to avoid having children.

'I promise! All I want is Hiroo,' she'd answered passionately. 'Elder sister, it's a *yubikiti*-promise.' Ohatsu had linked her finger in mine, then burst out laughing in her enchanting way. 'If I break my promise, I'll have to cut off my little finger, won't I?'

How childish my young sister is! My heart leapt towards her that day. Three months later she came

17

running into Maeda's garden, her little finger bandaged tight.

'I – I broke my promise, *nei-san*. You see,' said Ohatsu, 'Hiroo *insisted* that we have an heir. How could I go against my husband? But I was faithful to our *yubikiti*-promise. I did cut off my little finger.'

'You – cut it off!'

'Well, I didn't quite succeed. I fainted before I'd really cut it through.' Chatsu held up her wounded finger. 'I'm glad I didn't manage it. I hate anything deformed, *nei-san*! I hate ugliness,' cried Ohatsu, and, bending over a rose bush, tore off a dead leaf with a vehemence that frightened me.

I had kissed her bandaged finger, and as I held her childish body in my arms, I'd felt that she was *my* Ohatsu again, the little girl I'd brought up after our mama – a flaming torch – had thrown herself in the river on the day of the bomb. But as I rocked her to and fro, fright filled me. To try and cut off one's finger! What other gestures and desperate acts might Ohatsu not attempt?

'Tea! Rice cakes!' Small sister slides under the blanket with me. 'I hid these three cakes in my room, *nei-san*. I love to nibble things in the night.'

'Glutton!'

'No, no! It's my little son who gets hungry about this time.' Ohatsu laughs happily.

How cosy to lie with my sister on my soft *futon*! She snuggles up to me conspiratorially.

'We can have a cake and a half each. No, come to think of it, I'd better have two and you just one. I'm *two* people now, and have promised the ancestors that Hiroo's son will be born plump.'

While we munch our rice cakes and wait for the water to boil, Ohatsu tells me that each morning when she fulfils her duties as the *yome* of the house, putting rice on the family altar for the benefit of Hiroo's forefathers, she makes sure to give them double portions. Lately she has given them candy, too, to earn their goodwill.

'Tomorrow they'll get a little of the noodle dish left over from tonight's supper,' Ohatsu tells me. 'You know, elder sister, I'm sure that Hiroo's *hotoke* like me – especially his father. His papa-san's coloured photograph smiles down at me, looking so like Hiroo.'

'Except that your Hiroo does *not* have snow-white hair.'

Ohatsu laughs, peers under the spirit lamp's lid. 'Our tea's ready, *nei-san*!' she cries and pours water into the stone teapot. My sister does things so beautifully. Tending flowers and plants daily, her hands have accustomed themselves to move with gentle care.

'Your cup!' she cries. She bows from the waist, respectfully offering me a wafer-thin tea-bowl from which a painted rose smiles up at me. Then she pours herself a bowl. How nice we're having it. But as Ohatsu kneels beside me, she catches sight of a slip of paper sticking out from beneath my pillow.

'The cablegram! Do you sleep with Willoughby-san's cablegram beneath your pillow?'

To lie – or not to lie? Should I pretend that Sam's cable slipped under my pillow *by accident*? Thank goodness, wise Aunt Matsui has taught me a way out. 'In a ticklish situation always answer with a counter-question,' is her advice.

'Do you remember that when Sam-san first came to lodge with us he was crazy about *you*, Ohatsu?'

'About *me*? That foreigner? I can't bear *haro-sans*!' cries Ohatsu passionately. 'Why is your American coming back to Japan? To make money?'

I put down the Shimitzu family's fragile bowl so brusquely that it almost cracks. Heavens! some of the tea's spilled over on the *tatami*.

'Sam Willoughby doesn't care about making money!' I snap back, and from the hitch in my voice I realize that my heart, like the tea-bowl, has spilt over. 'Sam-san's chosen to be poor. He left his step-father's business to study for a science scholarship. In fact he had to take a night job in a cafeteria.'

Hà! Have I let the cat out of the box, to use one of Sam's pretty expressions? Does my sister realize what this young American has come to mean to me? Can she guess that we've written to each other for years? Does Ohatsu *grasp* my craving for a full personal life, for gaiety, for fun? Oh, Sam! You're so wonderfully light-hearted! And much nearer my age than dear old Maeda.

'Maeda-san's having a moon-viewing party Tuesday, and he invites you,' I say. (Always change subject when you're about to lose your temper, Aunt Matsui advises.) 'Will you come, Ohatsu-san?'

'A party!' Ohatsu cries delightfully. 'Of course I'll come! I'll wear my new *buyens*. It'll be my last outing before the baby arrives.'

But then she throws me a funny look from the corners of her eyes.

'*He* won't be there, will he, *nei-san*? If – *he's* coming, I shan't show up.'

'*He?* Can't you call him Tanso?' I snap.

Now I'm exasperated with Ohatsu! Because Tanso's withered hands horrify her, he's to be kept away from Maeda's *tsukimi*-party. She's shrunk her whole world to the size of a bird's nest, inhabited by herself, by Hiroo and by their unborn child.

I scold my sister, but even as I speak to her I see that her attention's wandered. She's harkening, head tilted. Springing to her feet, she runs to the open *shojii*, leans out.

'Do you hear, *nei-san*? Owls hooting! It's a bad omen.'

Ohatsu stands there motionless, her thin hands clasped. Not a sound troubles the August night, but I know it would be useless to contradict her. The owls are there – for her.

'Now! *Now* do you hear?' Ohatsu whispers. On her face is that look of tenseness that always fills me with alarm.

'*Anata!* Come back to bed!' I hear my brother-in-law's voice.

A look of adoration sweeps into Ohatsu's face.

'Hiroo! He's calling me, elder sister. My – my husband wants me, *nei-san.*'

She sends me her inimitable smile and flies off to their room. By the *fusuma* she stops to wave to me, then slips behind it in her long night kimono.

I lie peering after her, and now I feel my eyes closing at last. The herb tea's taking effect, thank goodness! Oh, I must hasten to doze off before my own hidden fears start crying. The night's still and calm. But we all hear owls hooting in the dark gardens of our minds.

3

'PLEASE excuse our poor moon-viewing dumplings.
Dozo! I made them.'

Oh, it's exhausting, this proffering of my bamboo
tray while repeating the polite formulas! Never mind.
It's such a lovely night – just right for Maeda's moon-
viewing party. An hour ago, as his guests knelt in a
row on the *roka*, a great yellow cheese heaved itself
into the sky. The moon! Its turning up so punctually
was reassuring.

A slight miscalculation, though. I'd counted on
Maeda's art students taking three dumplings each.
Smacking their greedy lips, they've already grabbed
four! Of course they don't stand on ceremony with
me. We meet every day, seeing that I cook their mid-
day rice, and in the evening clean their paint brushes.
Giving them a wink, I snatch my tray out of their
reach.

(Oh, dear, was that our gate screeching? No, just a
cricket rubbing its legs. I'm truly distracted about
Tanso's not showing up! Could he have been taken by
the police? His delinquent friends are ever ready to
receive him when despair drives him to deeds of
violence which repeat the actions of his childhood. For
until Morioka took him in, wasn't Tanso one of those

23

marauding *furoshi* that roamed in bands through shattered Hiroshima?)

'Moon-viewing and saké are as inseparable as two lovers,' jokes Maeda, as he glides up to me in his black party kimono. 'It's time to bring out your iced wine, Yuka-san.'

My *sensi's* smile has become as much part of his features as his sad eyes or his serene forehead. Dear Maeda! His personal suffering and concern for others lie behind that tender look. 'For a perfect hostess!' he says, taking a camelia from his *obi* and handing it to me. (I can't imagine this old painter not wearing a colourful flower.)

It's at this moment that I catch sight of Professor Morioka coming in by the garden gate. Ah, just what I'd feared! The famous professor nods to our guests in his unceremonious way, but his eyes roam about for the boy he adopted when his own was blown to dust. Sam used to say something about eggs and baskets. Well, Morioka-san's put *all* of his eggs into basket Tanso!

'Ah, Morioka-san, do come over here!' cries Maeda.

The professor joins us on the lawn. As I bow, I try to make my face as expressionless as one of my own dumplings.

'You have honoured our humble party by coming early,' I say with the air of surprise that wily Aunt Matsui taught me. 'How kind of you to get here so soon, Morioka *Kyoju*.'

But the clever professor sees through me. The truth is that the moon, as well as our party, is at its zenith. Ta-ta-ta! sing Maeda's young painters. They have started to dance on the grass, doing a Western swing with Japanese variations. Ta-ta-ta, they sing, leaping about.

'My son hasn't arrived yet?' the professor asks me, wistfully watching Tanso's fellow-painters amusing themselves in ways forever denied his adopted son.

'He spoke of going somewhere first,' I invent glibly. 'There are so many *tsukimi*-parties tonight.'

Morioka-san sends me a look like a stab. *Hà!* I know only too well what the professor is thinking. It's *I* who am to blame for his, Tanso's, absence. As if I were a general, capable of ordering my heart about! (Perhaps if I hadn't received that cable from Sam four days ago, I could have *continued* to pretend. Everything's changed now.)

'A word with you, Nakamura-san.'

What brusque ways this great professor has! Morioka snatches a moon-viewing dumpling from my diminishing stock and pops it into his mouth whole. Perhaps the celebrated radiation physicist's many travels abroad have caused him to forget our Japanese manners. His modern-style behaviour puts my teeth on edge.

'Nakamura-san,' he cries, swallowing as quickly as a dog. 'I'm travelling up to Tokyo next week for the August sixth anniversary. Would you come along as my – interpreter? Many English-speaking delegates are expected.'

I bow and bow again. Above the rim of my fan, I send the professor a smile that gives nothing away.

'A thousand thanks, Morioka *Kyoju*,' I murmur. What on earth lies behind his invitation? The professor promptly informs me.

'Perhaps Tanso will accompany us,' he says, and sends me a funny look. 'It would do him good to get away from Hiroshima for a bit.'

Heavens! He's spilled beans now. Tanso, more often drunk than sober, is in the black books of the police, and Morioka-san's haunted by the thought of his son's landing in jail. Yes, it would 'do Tanso good' to leave, but the trip might turn out most dangerous. Of course I long for Tokyo. (Perhaps I could fetch Sam when his plane comes in.) But what about Tanso – and me?

> '*Round, round round*
> '*Like a bowl of tea.*
> '*Round, round round*
> '*The moon looks down on me.*'

The young painters are singing that jingle which children love. Then one of them calls on Maeda to recite a moon-poem, and when they all urge their master, he recites the opening lines of one of our moon-*tankas*: 'Oh, moon, radiant moon, must you too hasten away?' But he stops abruptly and his gaze lingers on the night sky. Did Maeda think of his wife, who also had to 'hasten away', speeded on by the atom bomb? His smile floods back as he continues his recital. According to my selfless *sensi*, it's egotistical ever to show personal pain.

Sà! The gate! And this time it's not a cricket. When I turn my head, I see two policemen letting themselves into Maeda's back garden. With an effort I collect myself, determined to stop these uniformed gentlemen from spoiling Maeda's *ubiki*-party.

'What a beautiful moon,' I say, smiling and bowing, but my attempt at graciousness is met by an icy stare.

'Is Morioka Tanso here? He's wanted for smashing a shop window.'

'Morioka Tanso?' My face expresses incredulity. Remembering another of Aunt Matsui's ruses, I burst out laughing. 'Excuse me, please, but the idea of inviting that — that *ruffian* to a *moon-viewing party*! Why — it's comical!'

'Sorry, *oku-san*. You see, we were informed.'

I shake my head, smile, bow again.

As I watch the policemen bicycling away, my face is perspiring. A narrow squeak! Mopping my temples, I hurry towards my room, taking the back way through the sheltering bamboo trees. A dash of water, a comb through my hair, and I'll be presentable again.

Oh, my safe little room! I wish I could fold you in my arms, together with my sleeping children and my

27

snoring Mrs Bullfinch. Kneeling before my dresser, my braids in my hands, I throw a grateful glance around my moonlit haven. Within these four walls I gathered together the shreds of my life after Fumio's death. I've woven those threads into a whole, and I'll let nothing – no, *nothing* tear my life to pieces again.

'Tanso!'

He's stepped so suddenly through my open *shojii* that I cry out in fright. Tanso's eyes, half hidden by his beatnik bangs, are blood-shot, and he has a gash on one cheek. Oh, he's in a terrible state! The painter's smock which he wears at all times (its roomy pockets are kindly homes for mangled hands) is ripped in many places. What a good thing that the police didn't see my besotted friend! He stumbles towards me, kneels – and buries his bleeding face in my hair.

'What has happened?' I whisper. Of their own accord my fingers reach out to touch his wounded cheek. 'Oh, my poor Tanso!'

But Tanso lurches to his feet. His eyes flash in his grimacing face.

'Keep your pity!' he shouts at me. 'Yes, keep your pity. And – and damn you to hell, Yuka!'

I beg him to talk lower, but Tanso keeps on shouting.

'Why don't you go to your American friend? Don't let me stop you! You can't save me. No one can save me – *no one*, I say.'

Oh, I've got to take this situation in hand! Another

moment and his honourable father will come hurrying. What a meeting!

I spring to my feet, but before I can move, Tanso pushes me aside. He goes stumbling towards the open *shojii*. He's bent on making a scene, as so often before – bent on ruining the evening and bringing shame to the man to whom he owes everything.

It's fate, in the form of my little boy's toy dove, that comes to my rescue. 'Ko-ro-o!' it coos as Tanso puts his drunken foot upon it. And then a second drawn-out, 'Ko-ro-o!' Its red glass eyes gleam in the moonlight.

Tanso halts. He looks about my moonlit room and his eyes come to rest on my children's *futons*. Tanso stares down at my fat *dakko-chan*, whose hands are folded on the bed cover.

'I once had hands like that,' he says after a pause. His voice is low now, I can scarcely hear him. 'I was his age when mine were destroyed – when *I* was destroyed.'

I don't speak. It's the first time I've heard Tanso talk openly of his claw-like hands. I mustn't interrupt him with humdrum reflections.

'I looked evil in the eye that day,' he continues, and his gaze is still on my *dakko-chan's* chubby paws. 'For the atom bomb's the symbol of evil – did you know that, Yuka? And he who's looked evil in the eye is – doomed!'

Tanso gives the dove a violent kick that sends it

flying across the floor. He bursts out laughing. It's so jarring after his words of despair that I put my hands over my ears.

'Peace doves!' shouts Tanso. 'Could anything be more ridiculous – the manufacturers of machine guns and bombs turning out *peace doves*? What a joke! And meanwhile idiots like 'the professor' go about gabbing at peace meetings – that is to say, when those 'peaceniks' aren't fighting each other like rabid dogs. The *fools*!'

I don't dare move. Anything I say might increase Tanso's rage, driving him to make a scandal before our honoured guests. He gives the dove a second kick, but loses his balance, falls on my *futon*. His arms are stretched out on either side and the two mittens graze the floor. A few seconds later I can hear his drunken snoring.

> '*Round, round round,*
> '*Like a bowl of tea.*'

From beyond the open *shojii* I hear the laughter of Maeda's young painters. Ah, how healthy, how exuberant they are – these fellow-students of Tanso! What fun to sing childish songs to the moon!

> '*Round, round, round*
> '*The moon looks down on me.*'

Suddenly I want to get away from Tanso – want desperately to escape from our common sadness. Like the arms of an octopus, the tentacles of the *gembaku* have been strangling me for too long. I want to live. Yes, *now* – while there's yet time! With a flash of joy I remember Morioka's invitation to travel up to Tokyo. Oh, I'll be going! Nothing can hold me back.

4

SHOULD I pack my *homongi*? Or won't I need my 'visiting-kimono'? Well, need it or not, I'll take it to Tokyo. Too bad I don't own a suitcase, but never mind. I can tie up my few belongings in a *furoshiki*. Oh, packing's a nerve-wracking job! And Mrs Bullfinch makes me more nervous yet by complaining in her cage.

(What is it, darling? You're hot? But it's August, Mrs Bullfinch, so what do you expect? There! I've moved your cage into the shade. Now will you let me get on with my packing?)

Oh, it's delightful to kneel by the open *shojii*, folding my belongings and putting them in, then changing my mind and taking them out again – chatting to Mrs Bullfinch, humming a tune. By craning my neck I can see Maeda's art students painting away on their canvases. Well, they mustn't dawdle. In ten days the annual Hiroshima picture show will be opening and they don't want to disappoint their master. Strange that of all of them, it's Tanso who's most talented, even though he has to paint with his brush tied to his wrist like Colot. (Colot? Corot? I'm unable to keep those l's and r's apart.)

'Mi-chi-ko!'

I can tell from the way my daughter waves back at me that she's praying no one will stop her. She's on the way to her 'atom-bomb shelter', no doubt. I have to smile as I think of her crouching beside it, worriedly counting its inmates to see that none has slipped away. Not that it's anything to smile at, really. Isn't it her fear of another *gembaku* that made Michiko build her Noah's ark? That same fear's shared by all us survivors.

'*Sà-à!*'

Her scream of despair reaches me from the direction of the shelter. Oh dear! Scarcely a day passes that Michiko's pile of cans doesn't tumble down and her bugs and beetles go scurrying off on spindly legs, Michiko in hot pursuit. Poor *mushi*, they don't know why they're being so lovingly protected!

I hasten across Maeda's lawn and find my little daughter digging frantically with a pointed stick.

'His wife – got away.'

'Whose wife, Michiko-chan?'

(No, I mustn't speak in a flippant voice! My girl's set on protecting her beloved *mushi* from the fate that overcame her father and a hundred thousand Hiroshimans.)

'The worm's wife,' she replies gravely. 'After the next atom bomb falls on us, there won't be any baby worms left to carry on. My worm must have a wife to make children, you see, Mama.'

'Yes, I see.'

Meanwhile Maeda himself has appeared on the

scene. As if he, too, were concerned about the survival of worms, he begins looking for the missing *mushi*. In a moment he holds up the wriggling creature between his fingers.

'Got her!' cries Maeda. He drops the worm back into the tin can that is her home, then tucks up the sleeves of his *yukata* and sets to work helping Michiko rebuild her shelter.

'Tanso's just finished his painting, Yuka-san,' he tells me as he places a large stone on top of the pyramid of cans. 'It's an outstanding piece of work. First rate! I believe it's only through recognition of his talent that this delicate youth can be saved from despair. Come with me and I'll show you the picture.'

But – what's happened? Approaching the studio, I see that all the young students are gathered about one canvas. A scuffle's taking place. Suddenly Tanso breaks away and comes running towards us in the direction of the gate. Red paint drips like blood from the brush tied to his wrist, and as he dashes past, his eyes meet mine. Oh dear! I can read in them the same desolation, the same frantic despair as the other night when he hid his bleeding face in my hair.

'*Sensi*, come and see! Please come, *sensi*!' the students are calling. But there's silence as Maeda walks towards the canvas and stands before it. Ah-h! Tanso's done it again – ruined his painting. Over an imaginary city of the future fresh red paint drips from the sky.

What's that evil object Tanso has sketched in? A –
bomber plane? Another *gembaku*?

'That Tanso – he's mad!' one of the students murmurs. 'Mad Tanso.'

But Maeda has left the workshop without a word.
He walks across his lawn to the big smooth stone on
which he sometimes sits in contemplation for hours.

'*Sensi*,' I whisper, kneeling beside him on the grass.

'Yuka, I've failed.' Maeda's voice is so low I can
scarcely hear him. 'I thought that Tanso might be
saved through recognition of his talent. I was wrong.
That shows that I am still ignorant of the workings of
the human heart.'

Gently Maeda touches the smooth surface of his
beloved rock.

'I must think it out,' he says. 'Yes, I must try to
think it out. Leave me, Yuka-san . . .'

Ping! Ping Ping! Ping! Ping!

The voice of my old friend, the kitchen clock,
reaches me across the lawn. (It's one of the few objects
I was allowed to keep when Fumio's and my home was
sold at auction.) There's not a minute to lose! Ohatsu's
waiting for me, as every evening when Hiroo takes his
mother to her Buddhist temple. If I don't hurry – and
even if I do hurry – I'll be late . . .

'*Nei-san!* I've been waiting for you. Oh, I thought
that something – *terrible* had happened!'

Small sister's voice is taut, her eyes stare. Oh, why
can't she take things lightly? Why can't she laugh at

35

someone's being fifteen minutes late? Kneeling at the *fusuma* in the flowing kimono that hides her pregnancy, Ohatsu gazes at me tragically. How beautiful she is!

But now a little smile steals into her face. Her panic's subsided with my arrival, and she's already forgotten the cause of it.

'Look, elder sister!' she cries, putting something pale blue in my hands. '*Tabis!* I knitted them. Blue for a boy, you know!'

'And it will be a boy?'

'Yes, yes, it *must* be! Hiroo'd never forgive himself if he didn't present his honourable *hotoke* with a male descendant. You *do* think it will be a boy?' She asks me, so tensely that I put my arm around her shoulder. Oh, my poor over-anxious little sister!

'I *know* it will!' (I've promised Ohatsu everything she's wanted since she was a little girl.)

Oh, it's bliss to be together here, to speak in intimate voices, to laugh about nothing at all! Happily I look about me. In this little garden room Ohatsu's baby will spend his first hours on earth. His portable basket stands in one sun-drenched corner and fluffy baby toys lie scattered on the *tatami*. (I suspect that Ohatsu plays with them. She dearly loves toys.) As her garland of lucky cranes suspended across the ceiling goes 'Sh-h! Sh-h!' in the evening breeze, small sister smiles at me from the corners of her eyes. She picks up her scissors and starts cutting out more cranes.

36

'They say that one must make one thousand, five hundred if they're to bring *real* luck,' Ohatsu says.

The tip of her tongue shows between her teeth as she cuts. She sighs with delight as snowy birds emerge from her quick-snipping scissors.

Now's the moment to broach the ticklish subject of my trip to Tokyo. I dread her reaction!

'Of course I shan't leave if you don't want me to,' I assure her, trying not to sound too excited at the prospect ahead. (I do so like to have fun! I've a bad tendency to light-heartedness, I know.) 'I'll only be gone for a few days,' I promise my sister.

Thank heaven, Ohatsu laughs. 'But the baby isn't due till the third week of August, *nei-san*. And I'm so busy cutting out lucky *ori tsuru* that I'll scarcely miss you.'

Small sister's in a light-hearted mood now. Everything's lovely. But as the evening shadows slant across her plants outside the *shojii*, she suddenly stops cutting out. How quickly my sister's sensitive face can change from joy to anxiety!

'*Nei-san.*'

'Well, what is it?'

'What will happen to my potted plants while I'm having the baby?'

Ohatsu reaches out to feel a limp petal, and as she does so an insect darts from the flower's cup – zoom! My sister's tense glance rests on the thirsty flower. (Oh, I hate the frown that puckers her forehead! It reminds me of her 'bad' days.)

37

'You see, *nei-san*, they need daily care. Hiroo's mother is old, and she'll forget. I thought, if you didn't mind, that I'd ask Michiko to look after them.'

'*Michiko!*'

There's exasperation in my voice. Why Michiko, not *me*? I feel quick tears come to my eyes, even as I think with love of my dependable little girl. Oh Michiko, Michiko, I wish I were like you! To look at we're similar as two berries, but inside . . .

'Do you think that aspirins are good for plants?' Ohatsu is asking me. 'I'm going to tell Michiko to give them melted aspirins whenever they look down in the mouth. You see, your Michiko cares! For – everything.'

On small sister's hand the insect from the flower has alighted. Confidentially it perches there, its pink antennae waving happily. I think of its brothers and sisters whom my daughter is 'protecting' in her bomb shelter. Yes, Michiko *cares*. Is that her secret? Is that what makes Michiko – Michiko?

5

FANCY being on a great train – on the dashingly-modern Tokyo Express itself. Oh, I am *too* lucky.

If my friend, Keiko-san, hadn't drilled me so thoroughly in English, if Professor Morioka hadn't needed me both as interpreter and as 'bait' for Tanso, then I wouldn't now be sitting in our steel giant hurtling through the waving rice fields. The railroad administration is more than kind. It's arranged things charmingly for the honourable passengers – benches on which they may sit or kneel, shining cuspidors for those who like to spit, and a loudspeaker that keeps telling us of the train's speed, the time of day and other thrilling items.

Unfortunately, the August heat is at its sweatiest. All the gentlemen have taken off their jackets, and not a few have gone so far as to take off their trousers too. If only we ladies might follow their example! The thought makes me giggle.

How pretty, the young railway lady who trips down the aisle, squirting icy eau-de-Cologne on everyone! Famous Professor Morioka gets an extra large squirt. The great radiation physicist has followed the pleasant summer custom of divesting himself of his outer apparel, but although he sits by the window in his

39

underclothes, he perspires so profusely that I decide to get out my fan and cool him. For four days now I shall be in the service of the professor and his son, and I must do everything to please these gentlemen. Isn't the satisfaction of men's wishes the true happiness of women?

A minor catastrophe, though! I can't find my sandalwood fan. In the rush of leaving I must stupidly have left it behind. To be sure I could buy a cheap paper fan at the next stop, but meanwhile there's nothing for it but to pretend not to have noticed the professor's perspiring face. I shall appear engrossed in examining the farewell presents which were given me at Hiroshima station. If I utter little cries of delight, Morioka-san will never guess my ruse or blame me for being remiss in fulfilling my duties.

It's a good thing that we're taught the art of gift-unwrapping as children. Everyone in the coach is watching me as I take care not to show greed but maintain an expression of smiling unconcern while I untie the first parcel. *Mà!* A volume on flower arrangement from my brother-in-law. What an unusual farewell gift! (Perhaps a hint that women ought to remain in their homes and gardens, rather than dash off on jobs, like the '*après-guerre* girls'?) I hold my breath as I unwrap the dainty tissue paper of the next parcel, which gives out a most unpleasant smell. The Lucky Fish that small sister sent me as a *giri*-gift is beginning to stink in the heat. Well, never mind – what's one

40

smell more or less on a steaming August day? Peeping inside my children's farewell package, I see a mess of melted chocolate, quite unfit to offer my fellow-passengers. (I hope they won't think me impolite.) Luck changes when I open the next parcel, from Maeda. What a happy coincidence! A green paper fan!

'May I cool your face, Professor Morioka?'

Dear me! The professor's fallen asleep. There's a sad look on his face that makes me want to wake him, but for a woman to wake a man wouldn't be seemly. I'd fan Tanso instead, only he's slipped out of the coach, bent on getting drunk, no doubt. Is that why Morioka moans in his sleep, and why his mouth twitches? Tanso means the world to him! Ever since he lost his own son in the holocaust, Morioka's affection has been concentrated on this little *furoji* whom he adopted in his place.

Well, why not take advantage of my leisure to have a good look about our overcrowded carriage? What a lot of students! A group in the far corner are singing in unison, and when I harken, I can make out the words of a well-known peace song. No doubt they, too, are off to the August Sixth meeting in Tokyo. Four other youths, stiff as ramrods, sit beneath a framed photograph of our emperor which they have hung from the luggage rack. (I mustn't forget to bow to it as I pass on my way to the lavatory.) I sense at once that there's a tension between these two student factions.

A train, an express train – what an exciting place! In Hiroshima I see the same faces every day at Maeda-san's, as well as in the little food stalls where I do our marketing, but here, right opposite me, sits a real Tokyo beauty. Her skirt's as tight as the skin on a sausage and her blouse, too, is breathtaking. It has a 'plunging neckline' to which her companion glances with much interest. An inquisitive young man – but very handsome!

I wonder – could Sam by any stretch of the imagination be considered *handsome*? Small sister says that he looks like 'a pink pig', but then she abhors all *haro-sans*. Oh, shall I really see my friend tomorrow? Perhaps he's decided *not* to come to Japan after all and a second cable is winging its way over the Pacific at this moment. To allay my fears, I make up a gay *haiku* about Sam and me.

> '*Sam flies from L.A. – TWA,*
> '*Yuka from Hiroshima – Tokyo Express.*
> '*Will the two meet in the Imperial City?*'

What sweet chimes! The railway people are seeking to summon our attention. In a soothing voice the announcer tells us that we're coming into Osaka.

'O – sa – ka! We're coming into Osaka, gentlemen and ladies.'

So this is Osaka – that teeming town of five million people! An awful lot of them seem to have gathered in the station to greet Professor Morioka, the world-famous 'peace-prof', as Sam referred to him in his letters. The professor was seen off by a large delegation in Hiroshima, but that was nothing compared to this shouting crowd. Banners with anti-nuclear bomb slogans and pleas for peace wave beneath our window.

'Good luck!' roars the crowd. 'Success on your world tour! Banzai, Morioka-san!'

I sometimes wish Sam hadn't made me share his American sense of humour. How he would have laughed on seeing our distinguished radiation physicist acknowledge the crowd's salutation! Morioka-san has covered his front part with a spread-out newspaper, but his plump behind in brief underpants bobs up and down most comically as he bows, kneeling on the seat. I hide my lips behind Maeda's fan. I've *got to* giggle.

'Long live Morioka-san, the peace maker!' shouts the crowd. 'Long live international friendship!'

'*Down* with internationalism! Long live the Emperor!'

Heavens! It's those nationalist youths in the front part of our coach under the Emperor's picture. How unfortunate! They are screaming at the top of their lungs. Now a fist fight has started, the nationalist students pummelling the peace students so that blood flies. In retaliation for their blows, the peace students have torn down the Emperor's framed photograph. A provocative gesture indeed!

43

'Long live Peace! Long live Science!'

'Long live the Emperor!'

'Long live Morioka-san!'

Oh dear, the glass on the Emperor's photograph has got broken in the scuffle. A wild-eyed nationalist youth, clutching the picture in both hands, leaps towards Professor Morioka, evidently meaning to crush his skull and the fine brain that pulses underneath. Instinctively I throw myself before Morioka-san, covering him with my body. Broken glass spills over my hair before the youth is pulled away. As I dab at my temple, the police jump on the train, dragging off the trouble-makers, nationalists and 'peaceniks' alike.

'Are you hurt, dear Nakamura-san?'

I shake my head. The professor's question honours me. It's a privilege for a woman to render a little service to a man, and to save his life is particularly gratifying. I'm so glad that my body acted correctly of its own accord.

'I've got some mercurochrome in my handbag. *Dozo!*'

Who'd have guessed it? When I stepped on this train I'd have laughed if anyone had told me that I'd get to know an exciting young Tokyo lady with a plunging neckline – a provincial like me! While she dabs at my scratches, we smile at one another and exchange addresses in Tokyo. I am having all the luck today! Only I do wish Morioka-san wouldn't praise

44

my courage in front of strangers. He's so westernized! Seeing me hang my head, the clever man quickly speaks of something else.

'Those two enraged student groups portray our world, in microcosm.' Professor Morioka has seized the opportunity to harangue the coach. 'Friends, civilization is based on world peace. Without world peace it is doomed. But the barbarians – the ape-men – are constantly threatening.'

Ah, how comic! The unpredictable Morioka-san screws up his distinguished face to simulate rage. Baring his teeth, he shakes his fist at imaginary foes.

'You see how close man is to a gorilla?' Morioka-san laughs. 'By drawing back my lips, jutting out my jaw – like those young students just now – by squinting in hatred, I become almost indistinguishable from our primitive forefathers. *Hà!* We've just had proof in this very coach that man has not yet stepped out of the stone age. The tragic thing is that we propose hurling, not coconuts, but atom bombs at each other. *War!* Dear friends, that's an obsolete word for which I have substituted a better one – ENDLIFE. You see, it's either total peace – or the end of all life . . .'

'Tokyo, next stop! Tokyo in fifteen minutes!' announces the loudspeaker.

Heavens, it is high time to tidy up! As I hurry towards the lavatory, I almost trample on a scrap of cardboard from the Emperor's damaged photo. Snatching up the

45

shred, I put it in my pocket. What if one of the passengers should step on our Monarch's picture by mistake!

But the toilet is locked. Embarrassed, I knock and wait patiently. Nothing happens. After some moments I try again. Ah! The honourable train conductor, who's spent the day examining and re-examining everyone's ticket, is just hurrying past. He sees my plight.

'Been waiting a long time, *oku-san*? But it's strictly against the regulation to occupy the toilet longer than three minutes. *Hà!* I shan't have the rules flouted on my train,' the conductor cries. He takes a bunch of keys from his pocket and unlocks the door.

'Tanso!'

My hand flies to my mouth. On the closed toilet seat sits Tanso, his elbows on his knees, his chin on his wrists. The gruesome mittens cover his face – all except the eyes. Fixed on the wall, their gaze tells me better than words that Morioka's foster-son has reached his road's end. It is final desperation that I see there – the heart-breaking grief of a young man who once 'looked evil in the eye' and rejects a world preparing for ENDLIFE.

'Tokyo in five minutes. Please collect your baggage,' comes the voice over the loudspeaker.

About to turn back, I feel a tug at my sleeve. It's the conductor. Oh, how pale is this little man's face above his black uniform.

'Oku-san, the gentleman may stay. It is I, an employee of the railway administration, who gives permission. Five minutes,' he says. 'Yes, five minutes.' And he gently draws shut the door.

6

'Wow, what a stink!' cries Sam.

He screws up his nose and guffaws.

Goodness gracious, my friend Keiko's cat has dragged in the head of small sister's Lucky Fish and the whole room smells like a garbage can! Keiko's frowning at me. (She disapproves of Sam, not for being an American, but for being a *poor* American – and liking it.) I bite my lips so as not to explode with laughter, and I dash into the kitchen with the putrified object in my hand. Sam's at my heels.

'Hey, Yuka, you forgot his eye!' he cries, and drops into my hand a white fish eye which sends us a chilly stare.

How we laugh! The minute we're out of Keiko's sight everything seems easy and delightful. I can scarcely believe that it's years since the *haro-san* lodged in our house. (Oh, I must stop using that silly after-the-war name for Americans.) How nice that Sam's the same old Sam – ruffled hair, mussed seersucker pants, T-shirt! He looks just as carefree as he used to in Hiroshima.

Yes, small sister's fish really *was* lucky! We needed something amusing to get us over the first difficult moments of reunion. I've day-dreamed of Sam Willoughby for so long. And here we are together again, giggling about – smelly fish! Life's wonderful.

Keiko's doll-sized kitchen is so cramped that our bodies touch as we stand washing the fish off our fingers. That casual contact makes me feel quite faint. Quick! Make some silly remark to set us laughing again.

'Those glasses make you into a wise owl. After all those studies, I suppose you really *are* wise, Sam-san. But they haven't really changed your rooks.'

'*Looks*, honey – not rooks. Gee, now I know that I'm back in Japan! And I'd say that *your* rooks are pretty fine.'

I'm blushing. Oh, it's lovely to receive compliments again!

'No wonder I have to wear glasses,' Sam tells me. 'I was a self-help student and studied fourteen hours a day to get my scholarship, beside working in a cafeteria at night. And I'm still working fourteen hours a day in my stink-lab, *with* the scholarship!'

Yes, tall Sam does look worn. He's as skinny as a poor Japanese student, which endears the *haro-san* to me. How different he is from those wealthy American tourists on the Ginza! He's of another breed – yes, a finer breed. Didn't he prove that when he got himself arrested for joining sit-down protests at an atomic base? (How happy I was when I got the news! I knew then that he'd kept his promise, made at Fumio's death-bed, to carry on the fight against atomic war.)

49

There's the sound of plates being set down on the living-room table. Heavens, we've forgotten about Keiko!

'Do try and be friendly to her,' I whisper to Sam. 'Keiko's an awfully nice girl, really.'

'That tough cookie? Oh, she's a good-looker, I'll agree.' (His voice is enthusiastic. Perhaps it was a mistake to introduce them?) 'Do you know who she reminds me of?' Sam asks. 'My own ex-fiancée whom I wrote to you about – Miss Know-all.'

I point to the *fusuma* behind which Keiko's eaves-dropping, no doubt. Sam gives one of those comical groans that used to make me laugh.

'The scourge of Japan – the *fusuma*! No wonder that listening's become an indoor sport here. Look, honey —' The tall *haro-san* bends down to whisper. '— there's a cosy-looking bar across the street. Can't we – vamoose? I came to Japan to be with you – not with Keiko.'

He lays his big hand on my arm, just as the *fusuma* slides open. Sam and I jump apart.

'Some refreshments are ready – if you are,' says Keiko coolly.

Embarrassedly, the *haro-san* and I follow her, and we kneel by her pink plastic table. Gracious! I hadn't expected *suchi*. The putrid smell of 'Lucky Fish' still fills the airless room and the pyramid of flesh-hued *suchi* doesn't improve matters. I flutter my fan in front of Sam's face.

'A surprise, Sam-san! Keiko's prepared a little wel-come-meal for your first evening. What luck that *suchi's* your favourite dish,' I cry, giving him a warn-ing wink.

'*Suchi? My* favourite dish?' groans Sam. He hasn't caught on, but when I nudge him, he serves himself a generous portion. 'It certainly is – I mean, my favourite Japanese food. *Raw* fish! Yes sir! Yum-yum,' en-thuses Sam, but after his first mouthful sweat beads his brow. *Mà!* Will the young American – throw up?

'Might I open the *shojii* just an inch, Keiko-san?' I murmur, but my old school friend vehemently shakes her head. She explains that the din of her over-crowded back street is deafening, besides, its dust would choke us. I smile and give in. I know that it's not dust outside but the presence of Sam *inside* that accounts for that head shake. Keiko'd rather die from suffocation than have her prying neighbours get a peep of this sloppily-dressed American in *her* apart-ment!

'May one enter, please?'

'*Yoku irashai mashita. Dozo.*'

I *do* admire Keiko-san. This is the one person she didn't want here, but in a trice she's on her feet, delight-edly welcoming the wife of her employer! I, too, spring up. While we three women exchange drawn-out greetings, I see Sam place his paper napkin atop his *suchi* and deftly transfer the slices to his trouser pocket.

51

It's done in a second. Then he sits grinning happily. But in a minute everything's gone awry again.

'What's *this*?' Sam asks in his unceremonious way.

Simpering behind her fan, Keiko's visitor places a small pile of *giri-gifts* before the amazed American.

'Keep-sweet-relationship-gifts,' I tell him in a whisper.

I join in the good-natured giggling at the foreigner's ignorance of our elementary politeness custom. Next to plying people with food and drinks, *giri-gifts* are all-important in making and keeping friendships. But now my heart sinks as Keiko, kneeling by Sam's side, liberally replenishes his plate.

'The American's favourite dish,' she explains to her employer's wife. The two women beam at Sam! Between them they decide that no one else will touch the raw fish, leaving it all to our honoured guest. 'Now you must unpack your *giri-gifts*,' Keiko admonishes big Sam, as if he was a five-year-old.

'A pack of flowered tissue-paper. Why, thank you!' cries Sam. 'Just what I – need. And tooth picks! That takes a beating. What's this? A box of matches. Ah, I've always wanted to – er – own a box of matches.'

Sam's smile is so radiant that Mrs Fukara grows red with joy. Again things are beginning to go well, but suddenly Sam lifts his head in alarm.

'Do you hear that – in the kitchen? Mice! Yes, it must be a whole family of mice scampering about in there.'

'*Mice!* In *my* kitchen?' shrieks Keiko in dismay. And we dash out, all three of us. Turning my head, I receive a triumphant wink from Sam. Already the *suchi* — the whole lot of it — has vanished into his bulging trouser pocket. Oh, Sam really hasn't changed! I shake with suppressed laughter. I'm *too* happy. And in a little while, when we finally manage to escape, I shall be walking at the *haro-san's* side through the exciting streets of Tokyo. Just Sam and I.

'A little telly now!'

Twiddling the knobs, Keiko's kneeling beside her beloved television set, and while she expertly gets the picture into focus, she tells Sam that he's in for a second treat. The *sumo* championships!

'I'm a real wrestling fan, Willoughby-san,' cries Keiko gaily. 'I know you must be one too. Tonight we have a jumbo programme. All of three hours! What *luck* on your first night in Japan!'

'Look here, Keiko-san,' Sam tries to cut in. 'Yuka and I . . .'

'*Hà!* They're off! Slap-slap, like Billy-ho,' cries Mrs Fukara gleefully.

Formal Keiko has arranged us according to rank before her telly set, on the *tatami*. Sam's hunched up so close to it that his knees almost touch his long nose. Fukara-san kneels just behind him and Keiko behind her. It's quite correct that I shouldn't get even a glimpse of the screen. I'm two months and six days younger than Keiko, after all.

Thank heaven, everything's going smoothly. Of course, it's not quite what I'd dreamed about for Sam's first night in Tokyo – but are dreams meant to be fulfilled? Three hours of placid entertainment lie ahead of us, unless the American should faint from claustrophobia, heat and unfortunate perfumes. The naked *sumo*-wrestlers' sweating seems to permeate our airtight cubicle of a room, mixing most distressingly with the *suchi* smell.

'Say! The three-hundred pounder's tearing the gee-string off the two hundred and fifty guy,' cries Sam. 'It's getting exciting. Now he's tearing off little brother's leg. He-elp!'

'No, no, is *ashitori* movement,' explains Mrs Fukara, who seems also to be a *sumo* expert. 'While throwing or pushing, contestant *may* tear other fighter's limbs. Not quite *off*, though, Mr Willoughby. *Sumo* is gentle game. In year seven hundred after birth of *sensi* Christ, striking, kicking and maiming became forbidden. But *sumo* originally a killing sport, Willoughby-san. Before new, gentle rules, only one fighter was meant to remain in ring. The other – pouff! Dead.'

'So *sumo* has gone on as long as that?' says Sam, and to my dismay I hear his question end in a yawn. (Poor Sam! Hasn't he just flown in from Los Angeles?) 'How many centuries do you think this particular match will continue?' the *haro-san* asks blandly.

'Excuse?' asks Fukara-san.

She receives no answer. Instead a tiny snore issues

from Sam, but just as I'm thinking that nothing more unfortunate could happen, Keiko's tortoise-shell cat starts clawing at Sam's *suchi*-filled trouser pocket, miaouing greedily. Oh, I can't cope with this! No force on earth can stop a cat that has smelt fish. Distress and frustration have gone to my head, making the stifling room turn round and round. I wish those obese *sumo* wrestlers wouldn't keep grunting and giving each other smacks on their pendulous bottoms . . .

'Nakamura-san! Te-le-phone!'

That's a break, as Sam would say. My name's being shouted outside.

'It's the pastry-cook across the street. He takes my telephone calls,' Keiko explains. 'Hurry up, Yuka-san, or you'll be cut off.'

I dash into the fresh air, almost colliding with a bicycle errand boy balancing a pyramid of trays. Oh, I'm glad to get out of there!

'*Moshi! Moshi!* I shout into the mouthpiece, but Keiko was right – I've already been cut off. And here's Sam beside me, adding to the hubbub of screaming vendors and clacking *getas*.

'Listen, kid, I'm taking you out for supper. And right away,' he says. 'Understand? Oh, my God, where but in Japan would people get the idea of placing telephones *outside* their houses! Remember now – we're going out together, Yuka.'

I nod, looking up at the tall *haro-san*. But my eyes are such gossips! They give everything away. Yuka likes you, they tell Sam. Yes, Sam-san, I *do* like you – more than ever! In vain I try to hide my glance behind my quickly-raised fan. Too late! Sam's grabbed my hand and lifted it to his lips.

'Nakamura-san!' The voice that reaches me over the wire is like a shot in my ear. 'Morioka speaking,' it says. 'Something has – happened. Could you come here? Right away?'

'Come – there?'

But Sam snatches the telephone from my fingers. When I tell him it's famous Professor Morioka from Hiroshima, he caps the mouthpiece with his hand, begging me to rescue our evening.

'I've had more than I can stand, kid. I flew over all the way from the States to be alone with you, Yuka – don't forget.'

I choke with joy. It's the second time he's told me, so it must be true. But the professor can't be kept waiting. It's surely something serious to make him call me so late in the evening.

'Is it – Tanso?' I ask Morioka-san. (Oh, Tanso's always with me! He's like an aching tooth.)

'The police . . .' Morioka-san breaks off. I can hear him breathing heavily at the other end and know he's trying to steady his voice. 'They've arrested my Tanso, Nakamura-san. A drunken brawl in a bar. Just – just what I've always feared.'

A strange thing happens to me then. I forget all about the American, standing so close beside me. He could be in his faraway Los Angeles. I'm back in Hiroshima – Hiroshima after the *gembaku*. I see myself running among its ruins, and behind me comes a gang of half-naked *furoji*. Those orphans of the bomb will steal and stab in order to survive. (Their diet is rats and garbage, but the rats have given out.) They are gaining on me! One skeleton-like boy runs before the others, shouting threats as he bounds across the rubble of our city. Doesn't he look – like Tanso? Oh, I must run faster . . . faster . . .

Then I feel Sam's hands on my shoulders. How warm and comforting they are! He's trying to draw me back from my world of memories, knowing without my telling him, that the ghosts of Hiroshima are still chasing me. Ah, Sam knows all about my ghosts!

'It goes on and on, kid, doesn't it – Hiroshima. It goes on and on. My God, I guess that none of us will see the end . . .'

7

HOW PRETTY, this little dresser with its frilly nylon cover! Kneeling before Keiko's mirror, I open her pink jars and sniff the scent from a bottle shaped like a thin-waisted lady. Sam laughed when I told him that I'd never made up my face. Well, seeing that I'm here, why not seize a bull by a horn? Working 'Turtle Cherry-blossom Cream' into my cheeks, I'll think back on our outing of yesterday, Sam's and mine. I always love to go over, hour by hour, step by step, what I've done the day before. (Oh dear, was that the clock striking? Seven? I must hurry or I'll be late for our appointment in the Ginza.)

Yes . . . yesterday's outing. Sam was my guide, for Tokyo's really his city more than mine. He hasn't forgotten a single sight from his first visit here, and he had to show me them all. *Mà!* If only we'd stuck to playing tourists instead of letting ourselves get carried into a heart-to-heart! It's as I was feeding the Emperor's swans in His park that we began to speak of my bangles. Ting-ting, they went as I threw in the little bread pellets.

'You shouldn't have brought me such a beautiful gift,' I told Sam, but the *haro-san* only laughed. 'Junk!'

he said. 'Purest junk! But junk turns into jewellery on Yuka.'

My cheeks feel hot! Have I rubbed them too hard with the cream? No, I'm blushing at the memory of Sam's words. Junk into jewellery! Is that the foreigner's way of telling me – something more? I was so flustered by his compliment that I blurted out:

'It's wonderful that you *understood!* Bracelets. Thank you – for understanding, Sam . . .'

Heavens – the *shojü*! I've forgotten to close it, and the passing crab-vendor is staring at my face, smothered in beauty cream. I reach out to push shut the sliding panel, then hesitate. Isn't this *Tokyo*? To act shyly would be provincial, and besides, the honourable crab-vendor seems a pleasant gentleman. Making a comic face, he holds up a wriggling crab, whereupon I do the right thing – let out a squeal. Exactly what the crab-vendor-san wanted! We exchange a gay Tokyo smile before he saunters off, chanting, 'Live cra-abs! Live cra-abs!'

Where was I in my thoughts? Oh yes, feeding the swans in our Monarch's park, thanking Sam for the bracelets that would hide my ugly keloid scars.

'Kid, you're far too sensitive about those little bomb marks,' he'd told me. 'A few bangles hide them! No, it's not the scars on your arm but the scars in your mind that count, Yuka. Every mark on a person's body has its duplicate in his mind – same texture, same size and shape. And those mental scars never seem to heal.

59

There must be a hundred thousand scarred minds in Hiroshima!'

Sam jumped up from the bench. (Oh, he's so un-controlled, the *haro-san*! My little son's better at hiding his feelings than this tall American.) As I trotted after him, he was fuming away at the 'push-button generals' who still talk in terms of mega-deaths.

'I wonder if they list psychic casualties too,' the *haro-san* said. 'So many million mentally killed – so many million morally wounded. Oh hell – as if that would stop them!'

Sam shoved his fingers through his hair. It looked like wires standing on end. Suddenly I knew that I was going to get a shock.

'But I'm a fine one to speak of stopping anyone!' he cried bitterly. 'I'd better tell you now – I've been trying to ever since I arrived, Yuka. Truth is I've chickened out of the peace fight. Yes, I knuckled under when the going got tough.'

Stop it, thoughts! I don't want to remember any more. Quick, some powder to dust over Keiko's cream, and a dab of rouge. (No, Sam said that he hates lip rouge. All right, I'll just borrow her pencil and darken my eyebrows a bit.) Oh, what a wicked man, that college dean, to have told Sam to behave more 'moderately' if he wanted a scholarship! No more sit-downs, no more demonstrations, said the dean. As if, Sam cried, with his eyes flashing – as if one could act 'moderately' while trying to stop atomic wars!

'I've let you down, Yuka!' he stormed. 'I've let down Fumio after promising him to fight. I'm a stinking compromiser, out for myself!' cried the *haro-san* as he strode ahead through our Emperor's elegant gardens. He took one stride to my three. My heart was heavy – perhaps that's why my feet felt like lead in my light *getas*.

Oh, where's Maeda's green fan? Where's my handbag with the address of that Ginza bar? I'll be glad to get out of here, away from my thoughts and my own feeling of lack. For what have *I* done for peace in these years? Nothing! Like Sam, I've let Fumio down and allowed my personal life to take over. No different than most women, I try to tell myself. But that doesn't make it better. (Ah, thank goodness, there's my bag – and the address.) How sad it all is! Sad that we failed Fumio. Still worse that we failed ourselves.

* * *

'Whoa there!' cries Sam. 'Whoa!'

We've visited so many bars on the Ginza that his 'whoa!' makes me chortle, these being people, not horses. I swallow my giggle and bow to the young couple who banged into us as they came out of the rickety bar. They're so blinded with love that they can't see where they're going, but manage to mumble excuses for having stepped on the *haro-san's* extra-long feet. Ah, they look ecstatic! Love has melted their expressions, so that their faces look blurred in the light of the swaying lanterns. Only their lips glow red beneath cheeks that are white with passion.

'*Yurako-cho de aimasho . . .*'

My favourite song! How I adore the melody that drifts from this shabby bar. Maeda's pupils whistle it when they're in love. 'Meet me at Yurakocho station!' It's romantic! Sam and I harken, then without a word the impulsive *haro-san* grabs my arm and steers me into the hot dark room. (He says he prefers places like this to the brightly-lit Ginza cafés.)

'I want to dance with you. I want to hold you – Yuka.'

A ticklish situation. I've never danced Western-style and mightn't I betray my carefully-concealed feelings if I remain clasped in the *haro-san's* arms? Swiftly I sit down at a corner table with its one dripping candle stuck in a beer bottle. I fan myself with Maeda's fan and *will* my eyes to look calm.

'It's got late,' I murmur. 'The last bus for Keiko's district leaves at midnight.'

But Sam doesn't bother to answer. Oh, he's really *too* unconventional! Well, what of it? For me he's just Sam and I love all of him, down to his shrunken T-shirt, which squeezes his great frame. His arms with the fair hairs simply burst from the short sleeves, and his neck is dark with sunburn. As Sam watches the boys and girls dancing with their eyes closed, their cheeks pressed together like plums on a tree, his own eyes grow veiled. I, too, feel dazed. How to get over this moment?

'*Dozo*. Sam. What does your watch say?'

He bursts out laughing. (Oh, no one's as impulsive as the *haro-san*. I must learn to decipher his changing moods.)

'My watch doesn't say a thing. How could it? I've sold it. Sold my watch, sold my silver fishing trophies, sold everything I own to come to Japan. Sold my car too.'

'The one you liked so well? Jalopy?'

'Jalopy-san herself! Behold a millionaire, Yuka – a guy who possesses nothing but his own self.'

'*Yurako-cho de aimasho.*'

That tune again! I feel myself tingling. I've begun to love this dark little bar with its dripping candles, its couples in love. They're poor students, most of them. The girls wear jeans and their hair hangs down their backs.

There! The *haro-san's* jumped to his feet and his eyes are half closed as he reaches out his hands to me. Oh dear, I hope that we will keep our decorum! The floor's so crowded with enamoured couples that tall Sam and I can't move. I just stand there in his arms, pressed into his chest. And then my body gives a single shiver – that betrays all. Overcome with embarrassment, I pull myself free and make my way dazedly to our dim corner. Again the crooner murmurs, 'Meet me at Yurakocho station,' and the whole little room quivers with passion.

'Yuka! Yuka!' whispers Sam.

What a predicament! Sam's a Westerner, the situation's Western, and I don't know how to cope with it. Panicky, I raise my fan. One thing's certain – Sam mustn't see my face at this moment. Who can mistake the look of love?

He has pushed his chair close to mine, and draws my hand with the fan away from my face.

'Honey . . .'

'No, no, Sam. Don't speak.'

'Kid, I came to Japan not knowing what I'd find. Letters don't really tell anything. But now I know that you haven't changed – you're the same girl that I fell in love with years ago. And you just told me something, when we danced. You feel for me in the same way I feel for you.'

I begin to cry behind my fan. Sam's eyes, too, fill with tears, so I give him my second hand also. Squeezing them in his hot fingers, Sam tells me that he's loved me ever since the day when he came to Fumio's hospital to find me.

'There you were in the corridor, beside the stand where they sell fruit and things. You looked so forlorn. Yuka! Such a lost kid. Your head had fallen forward. Your neck looked like the stalk of a flower that's been broken.'

'I was buying an apple for Fumio.'

'I know. I wanted so much to stroke the back of your sad neck. I think I've never wanted anything so much,' Sam murmurs. He gives a shy laugh. 'And now

I still long to stroke the back of your neck – more than anything in the world . . .'

He can't go on. His voice is choked. Sam's face is white – like mine I'm sure.

'Let's get out of here! Can't we find a spot where . . .? Oh darling, I've got to be *alone* with you!' Sam bursts out.

He jumps up so suddenly that his knee knocks the table and our saké cups tumble over. Heavens, we haven't even touched our drinks! In desperate haste we hurry out of the dark bar, colliding with a couple that's just entering through the *shojii*.

'*Dozo*, excuse me,' I mumble. My hand is clasped in Sam's, and the *haro-san*, too, murmurs, 'Excuse us. Please excuse us.' As the couple stares at us I realize that there's a telltale look on our faces. Even the dim light from the paper lantern above the door reveals all.

So are we just as blind, as dazed with passion, as that other enamoured couple who bumped into us at this very door an hour ago? An – hour? Fancy that one's whole life can change in one little hour!

8

'THE nose-and-throat boy wants to take out your tonsils!' I shout. 'He'll do it free of charge, Sam.'

'My *tonsils*? *My* tonsils?'

Oh, it's not easy to make conversation as you wriggle along in a snake line, your arms linked to your neighbours! Before us dance an army of boys and girls from every corner of Japan. Like us, they're bound for Hibuya Hall, where Professor Morioka is to speak. It's exciting! I love the sound of our crackling torches, love to sing with the marchers. Our Hiroshima songs sound new, flowing from thousands of hot eager mouths. But the nose-and-throat student who has hooked himself to my arm is insistent.

'Tell the American that my offer stands,' he begs me. 'I like him. You see, he looks as if he didn't know all the answers . . .'

The medical student says something more that I can't hear, and I tell Sam, 'He'll do it for nothing – just because he likes you, Sam.'

The tall *haro-san* bends down to give the student's shoulder a squeeze.

'Thanks a lot, fellow,' he says. 'Listen, Yuka, you tell him that my tonsils are O.K. But if ever they're *not* O.K. I'll remember his offer. Tell him something else – tell him that I like him too.'

My fingers slip into Sam's.

'And *I* like *you* too!'

He can't hear what I say, but his fingers have heard my fingers talking, and they answer. Suddenly we're right back in that dark street near the bar, our arms around each other, as they were last night.

Someone behind us is shouting. 'Move on! Move on!' so we hurry our steps, with our neighbours on either side swinging along with us. Sam looks into their flushed faces and cries,

'What a swell crowd, Yuka! Tell me – who's she?' he nods towards the young girl whose arm is looped in his. 'And who's the guy in a taxi driver's cap?'

'Why – a taxi driver!'

'And me – am one actress,' explains the girl over the sound of the hissing torches. 'Making one film in Kyoto. French-style film – lots in bed. Come look? Plomise?'

'Promise!' answers Sam, and he'd say more, but a woman factory worker in our line makes a sign to him to tie his handkerchief around his head. Almost everyone's wearing a bandana with an organization sign.

'What peace group does the foreigner belong to in the States?' she asks, and I translate for Sam. As he looks away I realize he's heart-sick at not working for any peace organization. Well, so am I! I'm ashamed at myself! Suddenly Sam and I avoid each other's eyes, for we know we're shirkers. How I envy that exhausted-looking medical student, that too-thin actress from Kyoto! *They* have given of their time to march all the way to Tokyo. The emblems on their head-scarves tell me they've banded together with millions of other Japanese to battle against atomic war.

The park gates! Fortunately the American's recovered from his depressed mood as our section of the snake reaches the park's exit. Snatching his handkerchief from his pocket and Keiko's lipstick from my bag, Sam draws a Picasso peace dove and ties the cloth about his head. Our companions smile approval. Oh, Sam can always make people love him! My darling Sam-san! It's his special gift.

'Wow! This show certainly takes some beating,' he cries as our line prances towards the torch-lit hall. 'You don't seem impressed though. What's the matter, honey?'

I don't know what to answer. How can I tell Sam my thoughts? Fanning my perspiring face as our group waits for the traffic lights to change, I remember what my *sensi* told me. 'Peace-marches are fine. But now we need something new – that's what Maeda says,' I tell Sam. 'We're in worse danger of nuclear war than ever before, yet—'

'So what does he suggest?'

Sam's hand moves up to ruffle his hair – the old worried gesture. His bandana's in the way and his fingers make a smear of that poor lipstick pigeon. It looks as if the dove of peace were bleeding to death.

'Maeda says that *total commitment* is necessary. One must be ready to give up one's personal happiness,' I say, quoting my *sensi*. 'Maeda believes that few people have made those supreme sacrifices that will bring about a world without strife . . .'

I give up at that point. The singing has risen to a roar and Sam can't hear me. At the top of the steps of Hibuya Hall I catch sight of a familiar figure.

'My Professor, Sam!' I shout. 'Morioka-san. The one with the thick eye-glasses.'

But by now Sam's busy exchanging cards with the medical student and others in the line. How happy he looks! The young American loves to be in a crowd of friendly people. Tonight he'll add these visiting cards to the dozens he's collected from new acquaintances – or just gentlemen in the street from whom he happened to ask directions. And he's promised everyone that he'll send a letter from Los Angeles.

Goodness, stopped again! It's annoying, as we're only a hundred yards from the hall now. In the light of the torches I can make out Morioka's tense features. He's *so* Westernized! The professor ought to be looking light-hearted, since he's worried to death about man's dilemma, terribly concerned about Tanso's drama. But his puckered forehead looks like cracked parchment.

'Thinking about the professor and his son again?' Sam must have followed my glance. 'Honey, you care too much about people – always have. This Tanso's a great worry for you, isn't he?'

'Worry?' I laugh. I try to make my voice flippant because of Morioka's unseemly show of distress. 'I never worry, Sam. *Never!*'

(Oh, inside-face, inside-face, hiding behind my politeness mask, how fortunate that no one can see you! Everyone has an inside-face, and mine's a maze of wrinkles. It's Tanso who's responsible for a lot of them. Ah, my poor aching Tanso!)

'Hey! We're moving. Wake up, kid!' shouts Sam, and I realize that our group's begun to cross the street. They're singing again, one of our Hiroshima songs, and Sam hums the tune. It makes me feel very close to him, having all those memories in common.

'*Fu-ro-sa-to de*,
'*Ma-ta aō.*'

We sing as our group swarms up the thronged steps. *Hà!* Morioka-san flashes me a smile, which dries up as his eyes fall on my American companion. (No doubt the professor thinks of the *haro-san* as Tanso's 'rival'. Poor Morioka-san! He still tries to believe that his son can find happiness, like any other man.) Respectfully Sam greets him, and the professor smiles back with chill politeness.

'The young American radiation physicist? Tell him that I am pleased to see him here,' he says, and Sam flushes with pleasure when I translate. He has great respect for Morioka, whose name is famous even in America.

But now singing has broken out again, and it's so thunderous that Hibuya Hall trembles. I can well believe that over a million people are demonstrating for peace all over our country tonight! The professor and the other Japanese delegates on the steps join in 'Gembaku no hana'.

> 'Father – no more,
> 'Brother – no more,
> 'Friends – no more.
> 'No one – no more.'

Lucky that Sam doesn't understand the words of our atom-bomb song. For it's Hiroshima herself who cries out those words from the bottom of her lacerated heart. I swallow a little lump as I think of their meaning.

'Come, Sam-san. Dozo,' I say, hoping that he's noticed nothing.

The haro-san's taken my arm and we hurry towards the doorway through which the crowd's streaming into the hall. As we push ahead, I notice that someone's trying to do the impossible – squeeze himself out of the hall. But isn't that Professor Shinohara, Morioka's fellow-physicist and friend? Yes, it is! But how excited he seems! He's crying, 'Please let me through! Let me through!' waving people to either side. Then he signals to Morioka. (What can have happened? Has one of the foreign delegates not arrived? Will the programme have to be altered? I must certainly catch what this gentleman has to say to my professor.)

Mà! Have I heard wrong? I *must* have heard wrong. The hubbub's so great, one can scarcely catch the sound of one's own voice. As Morioka asks his colleague to repeat, I tilt my head and strain to catch the professor's words.

'I said your son is in trouble, my friend. Can you hear me? I said your son . . . he's just stabbed a man to death, Morioka-san.'

I let go of Sam's arm. Pushing and struggling, I try to get close to Morioka, who stands there without moving. His face is a grimace of pain. I bow to him. I put myself at his service in this moment of crisis. The professor seems dazed. Is he about to faint? I begin to fan his perspiring face. Dear me, how little one can do when someone has received a death blow!

'But – but it's not possible,' Morioka-san murmurs. 'Not physically possible. Why, Tanso couldn't even hold a weapon in his hand. His mitten . . .'

'Ah, but he tore off his mitten, you see. He'd been drinking – heavily. He grasped a knife, so it seems. A telephone call from the police . . .'

'Morioka-san! Morioka-san!' blares a loudspeaker above the doorway, 'Morioka *Kyoju*, you are wanted on the platform. The programme is about to begin. Mo-ri-o-ka-san!'

As the last syllable of the famous name rings out,

the whole street breaks into applause. Everyone's shouting *banzais* for the professor. At that moment a cluster of white doves are let loose and go circling above the great peace-fighter's head. Ah-h! How beautiful they are! How – innocent! Pure as snow, they fly higher and higher, then descend just like snow-flakes – into the green park that we've come marching across. Morioka's stricken eyes follow the doves as they settle in the trees.

'May I help you, Morioka *Kyoju*?' I whisper. I don't know how to express myself, but I want the great man to feel my devotion. 'Will you let me take you home? May I – call a taxi, Morioka-san?' I ask, bowing, bowing.

The professor turns his head. All at once his eyes flash.

'No! Thank you, Nakamura-san,' he answers. 'For I intend to go through with this.' The professor straightens his bent back and throws the crowds a smile full of hope and courage. 'This is the most difficult thing that I have ever done for peace,' I hear Morioka-san say. He walks slowly into Hibuya Hall.

9

THANK goodness, we'll soon be in Katase! But I'm the worse for wear. My hair's dishevelled, and I lost a *geta* as the *oshiva-san* shoved me on to the subway car, using his full strength to get us all squeezed in. Not that I blame the over-worked 'pusher'. When I told him about my mishap, he answered politely that scores of *getas* disappear in the Tokyo rush hours. Vanish! Pouff! Gone!

It's delightful now just to *sit* in the Katase bus after my battle. Like a live dog, this Greyhound on wheels seems to stop before every tree, every lamp post, giving me plenty of time to go over yesterday's events. No, I decide I shan't mention the name of Tanso to Sam – despite all the tears that I wept last night. How could an American understand why my friend has to commit crimes? Sam-san was in over-fed Denver, while *furojis* in their thousands ate rats, robbed corpses and stabbed adult survivors for a few rags. *I* understand why Tanso became Tanso. For *I* was in Hiroshima after the bomb.

'Ka-ta-se!'

I bow good-bye to the driver. Opening my green fan, I step off the bus, telling myself again that yesterday's happening mustn't be allowed to spoil Sam's holiday. Isn't that why I persuaded him to go to the sea this morning, promising to follow after I'd helped Morioka-san through the gruelling day? I don't want Sam to get mixed up in our Hiroshima drama, as he did once before.

'Hi there! Hey Yuka!'

What a lucky Sam! His country's etiquette doesn't forbid him from throwing his arms around someone in public. I must let him hug me, though it's most impolite to disgust people by public displays of affection. I love Sam. Yet my body stiffens in his embrace, and quickly he lets me go.

'I lost my *geta*,' I cry to get us over this emotional moment.

'Never mind. Just kick off the other!' Sam-san laughs and hurries me towards one of the clam stalls on the beach. 'We'll have a few wriggly molluscs, then wander down to the sea when it gets dark. I have it all figured out!' says the *haro-san*, ordering clams and saké in the same breath.

He's glowing. Maeda has told me that happiness is as real as the light of the sun itself, and that he once saw it blaze from the body of a great pumpkin. Today it blazes from Sam's sunburnt chest.

'Yep, I've got everything figured out,' he tells me again. 'Just leave things to me, honey.'

Am I apt not to? It's for the man to decide everything. I'm so sorry for the beautiful American ladies who are always being divorced or left behind, like

75

Sam's know-all ex-fiancée. (After all, says Aunt Matsui, it took Japanese women thousands of years to learn how charming it is *not* to be the boss.)

It's got dark now. The waning August-moon is as red as an over-ripe apple, and lop-sided, as if someone had bitten a third off.

'That's O-Tsuki-Sama up there,' I tell Sam-san.

'Quite a girl. Let's drink to her, honey!'

So we drink together to the golden moon and Sam asks me to sing for him, as I used to do when he lodged with us in Hiroshima. A moon-song, maybe? Singing will help me give vent to my feelings and stop me from bursting with love.

> '*Round, round, round –*
> '*Like a bowl of tea . . .*'

'Or like your face, Yuka,' says Sam. 'Round, round, round like my darling's face.'

He pulls me to my feet. Our uneaten clams look up at us reproachfully, but Sam's not thinking of food. He hurries me down to the beach, far beyond the snack stands and the late bathers.

'Yuka, we've arrived!'

'Arrived?'

'In our first home, honey! Look – I made our bed this evening and dug that sand pillow for your head. Isn't it time to go to bed?'

I press my cheek against the *haro-san's* arm.

On the beach beside the edge of the water Sam's

etched a bed, complete with a sheet designed in the sand with a big sand monogram, 'Y.W.' Yuka Willoughby? Yes, *Yuka Willoughby*!

'As we've just set up housekeeping, we haven't got much furniture,' Sam explains. 'Just a bed – and that big bath tub over there. The biggest bath tub in the world!'

I sink down on the sand. Oh, how soft it is! Joining me, Sam lies on his back, peering up at the stars which, thank goodness, are the only witnesses. He holds out his hand for mine.

'Tell the truth, Yuka, when we get to California that's about all we will have,' he says. 'A bed and a bath tub. I'm a poor guy, you know. And I'm apt to remain poor.'

California! I feel my heart pounding and throw my arm before my face. Am I really going to California – as 'Yuka Willoughby'? What a strange way to propose! (But wouldn't our use of a *nakano* seem equally strange to a Westerner? The idea of Sam's employing a go-between in order to marry me is just too comical.)

He sits up, pulls me up, too. Then the *haro-san* motions me to kneel by his side.

'What's her name – that honourable moon Yuka?'

'O Tsuki Sama.'

'O Tsuki Sama. Here, before your Japanese moon, let us marry, Yuka. Will you take me for your husband? Repeat after me: I take you for my wedded husband, Sam.'

Husband! Now I know that this is no American joke. Sam-san's face, lifted to the moon, has a grave expression, and I repeat slowly:

'I take you for my wedding husband, Sam.'

'Not wedding – wedded, Yuka. And I take thee for my wedded wife.'

I begin to tremble. But when Sam pulls me to him, I resist. I want him *too* much! He lets go of me, and then I cry out, for it hurts me physically not to be part of Sam. I hide my face in his chest. How his heart hammers! Or is it my own wild breathing I hear? I don't know. I no longer know who is Sam and who's me.

* * *

Gracious! The towel of dawn has wiped our sky clear of stars. We must have slept for hours in each other's arms. Before Katase stretches and stirs, Sam and I must be gone. I shake him gently.

'Wake up,' I whisper in his ear. 'Wake up, my darling.'

How natural that 'darling' sounds! It's the first time in my life that I've used a term of endearment, seeing that there are none in our language. Has my marriage turned me into an American so quickly?

'Ta-xi!' shouts Sam.

I scold him for his extravagance, and Sam, grinning from ear to ear, tells me that I've already taken on a 'wifely tone'.

'A good thing, too,' he says, 'for we'll have to save every penny for the family we'll have after we're properly married. I want a huge one. One wife-san and *lots* of little kid-sans!'

In the taxi we cling to each other. How quickly our auto eats up the miles that seemed to take the bus hours to nibble away! The lights are switching off and the early shopkeepers are sliding open their *shojii* when we roll into Tokyo.

'Hell! We've already arrived,' Sam wails.

'But we'll meet again in a few hours,' I console him when our taxi stops before Keiko's little house. 'I'll be ready for you at twelve, Sam-san.'

'Yes – at twelve.'

Oh, I'm too happy! Too lucky! I stand there watching Sam's taxi driving away, and I wave and bow.

'Nakamura-san!'

I give a start. Who can be calling out to me before the day's properly begun? Across the street I catch sight of the nice pastry-cook who owns that red telephone. He's signalling to me so energetically that the white flour dances from his fingers in the pearly dawn.

Hà! It must be Morioka-san calling, I think as I hurry across the ill-paved little street, stepping on a deflated toy balloon that some child forgot last night. (The shrivelled pink balloon makes me long for my own children.)

'A long-distance call for you,' says the pastry-cook. He pats away a yawn after his long night's baking.

'They tried to get you late last night, *oku-san*. You're to call the long-distance operator, *dozo*.'

Oh, I must force calm on myself! I'm glad that my voice sounds quite steady as I ask for the operator – and a little later I hear over the wire a voice that I recognize at once.

'Maeda-san!' I cry.

'Yuka, something has happened. You must take the plane this morning. The *plane*, I said – not the train. Can you hear me?'

I fight down an impulse to call out Ohatsu's name. But I mustn't show hysteria. (My *sensi* hates lack of control.) When I speak, it's as if I were asking the most everyday question.

'Is small sister all right?'

'Ohatsu has just had her baby. That's why I'm calling.'

'Is she – is she . . . dead?'

Now panic has gripped me. Despite my efforts, my voice sounds shrill and ugly. A tray with freshly-baked rice-cakes which the pastry-cook has set out to cool on the sidewalk rises and floats in mid-air. Maeda has to repeat twice that Ohatsu's well before the fact registers. My relief is too violent, and I sink to my knees on the sidewalk. I am sobbing. The pastry-cook hands me a glass of water, but impolitely I wave it aside.

'Ohatsu's baby wasn't due for two weeks,' I cry. A new fear has caught hold of me now. 'Is – is her child alive?' My voice is as hoarse as Maeda's own.

'Yes, yes,' he answers. 'But your sister wants you. Ohatsu *needs* you!' cries Maeda. 'Yuka – come at once!'

My fright grows. I don't really know what I'm afraid of, but I can hear terror in my voice. 'Maeda-san! *Sensi!* What has happened?' I cry, but there are only clickings and tappings in the ear-phone. Then there's a long mechanical wail, like a cat's E-e-e-z. The telephone operator tells me that Hiroshima has hung up.

I try to get to my feet, but stumble. The pastry-cook helps me up. What an endearing face the small man has! It's come to resemble one of his own rice-buns. His raisin-eyes glint with sympathy.

'I couldn't help overhearing, *oku-san*. Your call was from Hiroshima?' he asks in such a tone that I feel a shiver go down my back. What wouldn't I give to be able to shout, '*No!*'

Once more the tray with the golden cakes rises in the air. After floating about giddily, it resettles on the pavement.

'Hiroshima's my city,' I tell him, and it's just as if I'd made a shameful confession. For my city's the most sinister spot on earth, and we survivors are sinister too, with our tainted blood and bone marrow. 'I was born there. I'm a – Hiroshiman,' I whisper, and hurry off across the narrow back street.

Keiko's *shojii* are closed, and her tortoise-shell cat's asleep on the *roka*. Perhaps I'd better not wake the household, just take the first bus to Haneda airport.

Dear me, I forgot to thank the pastry-cook for his kindly glass of water! To omit to show gratitude because of one's distress shows a flaw in one's character, Maeda says. (Ah, how distracted his poor voice sounded!) Quickly I recross the street and, bowing, offer thanks.

'*Arrigato! Arrigato gosaimas.*'

Oh, I wish the honourable pastry-cook would not gaze at me with so much pity in his eyes.

IO

I'VE ALWAYS wondered how Hiroshima looked from the air – how the gulls from the Inland Sea saw it when they flew in over our swanky skyscrapers. Now I know. Lucky gulls! *They're* not aware that new Hiroshima's built on twisted iron girders and human bones – atop ashes of lost happiness. No imaginative person should arrive in our town by air – Sam less than anyone. (Oh, Sam, dear Sam, I must phone you as soon as I know what's happened – as soon as I've spoken to Maeda-san.)

Maeda!

I keep my eyes set on him as I hurry towards the terminal. Panic's overcome me, as it did this dawn when I spoke to my *sensi* on the long-distance wire. Why has Maeda come all the way to the airport to meet me? Is it – is it because he doesn't want me to see Ohatsu before speaking to him? Ah, whatever's happened to small sister, I'll put it right! Haven't I done just that since she was no higher than a flower stalk?

But my *sensi's* not alone. Beside him stands a white-haired man whom I seem to know. How strange! Isn't it Hiroo's father, with whom Ohatsu and I had the honour of drinking tea one day? Yet we also had the honour – of accompanying him to the grave. All at once I realize who this white-haired man really is. *Hiroo!* Hiroo with white hair! I press back a scream. He and Maeda-san both keep bowing to me as I walk towards them, and I stop to return their bows. As I hurry forward, the airport building seems to sway towards me. My *sensi's* voice reminds me that I must behave with decorum.

'If you have no other luggage, then let's leave right away, Yuka.'

'Yes, *sensi*.'

I make my way into the building, and not for a second have I dared meet the eyes of my white-haired brother-in-law. When I join Maeda-san in the bus that's to take us to Hiroshima, Hiroo is no longer with us.

* * *

'Now, *sensi!* Tell me now!'

We're sitting on his thinking stone in the garden outside his house, Maeda and me. But he still doesn't tell me. Instead he lifts his finger and points at the hot summer sky.

'The sun's heat hasn't yet been tapped and put to the service of humanity,' he says gravely, and I force myself to concentrate. 'The same thing's true of the force of love. All last night I sat here on my stone, thinking. And I decided this: if we humans don't soon tap the force of love, then we're lost. Irrevocably lost, Yuka.'

84

'The force of love?' I repeat.

'Yes. Love's force is as vast as the force of the sun. It could transform our world! Hatred rules now – the hatred that makes war possible – that made Hiroshima possible.'

Oh, he's stretching my nerves too taut!

'*Sensi*,' I cry. '*Sensi*, speak to me! Why aren't *dakko-chan* and Michiko about? Are they – all right?'

'Yes, yes,' Maeda answers quickly, 'I left the children with your aunt Matsui for a few days. They are well.'

I've begun to tremble. Hiroo's white hair and the fact that my children have been got out of the way convinces me that our family's been struck by an irremediable disaster.

'Maeda-san, what's wrong with small sister? Did her mind – snap? Is that it?'

Again Maeda shakes his head.

'Don't put me off any longer. *Please, sensi*,' I beg, and hear that my voice has risen to a cry.

Maeda stays quiet for another minute. He's as still as his own thinking stone. My old friend seems not even to be breathing.

'Prepare your inner self for great grief, Yuka,' he says at last. 'What I'm about to tell you is a type of tragedy new on our earth. Ohatsu has suffered an experience that many women may have to endure in the decades ahead. Yes, that's certain. Unless men tap the force of love! Ohatsu's son . . .'

Maeda hesitates. I look away from his anguished

face, fasten my look on a blue butterfly that has settled on my arm.

'Don't torture me, *sensi*. Tell me about Ohatsu's – son,' I whisper.

'It – it isn't a son, really,' he answers.

'*Speak! Dozo*, Maeda-san. Speak!'

'It's – a monster.'

Now the word has been said. It's the word that we of Hiroshima never utter because of our gruesome fears. In Maeda's beautiful little garden on this beautiful August day the word has been spoken. And I have a strange feeling that I have known all along that this would happen – ever since Hiroo, disobeying his father's wish, took irradiated Ohatsu for wife.

'Yuka, you must know the worst,' Maeda says. 'This is not a thing I can spare you. It's not a calamity that can be told you a little at a time.'

I sit motionless. I press my knuckles against my mouth.

'Yuka, the head of Ohatsu's child is like an egg. Its face has no eyes – no nose. It breathes through a slot, near the chin. Whether the poor creature has a brain, Doctor Domoto can't tell. I've seen Domoto, and . . .'

Maeda-san can't go on, but go on he must. He, too, has his hill of anguish to climb.

'Domoto won't pronounce himself as to the cause of this monster birth. Monsters are born everywhere, he says – but we Hiroshimans know that such births are far too frequent in our city. Ah Yuka, the seeds of

86

Hiroshima are tainted and they will blow about the world for centuries to come . . .'

Maeda-san's weeping. *Maeda-san!*

I watch his tears falling on the thinking stone. Ah, warm, small drops, you are dear to me! You belong to a world I've left for ever – the world of griefs and joys, of tears and laughter. I've entered another universe. In this last minute I've realized that we survivors are victims of a war that has no end, a war that began with the *gembaku* and which might wipe out the future.

I get slowly to my feet.

'*Sensi*, I'm leaving. There's a noon bus for Kiosoko. Please don't come with me to the gate,' I beg, afraid that my new face will frighten my gentle friend – gentle old Maeda who still can weep.

I hear the rustle of his kimono sleeves and know that my *sensi* understands and has hidden his eyes in its folds. His voice comes muffled to my ears.

'Only *you* – Ohatsu wants to see only you, Yuka . . .'

In Hiroo's house beneath the cypresses the *shojiis* are all closed. Neither Hiroo's mother nor the old *genan* are about. Are they crouching in some darkened room, swaying to and fro in sorrow? Slipping off my *getas*, I slide noiselessly towards Ohatsu's part of the house.

'May I come in? *Irasahi mashita*,' I murmur. I open her *fusuma*. '*Dozo, imoto-san.*'

I bow in the direction of Ohatsu's *futon*. The person I'm visiting is not my sister at all – she's not the girl whose lovely body I've tended since babyhood. Ohatsu-san belongs to a wholly new species – a species that perpetuates monsters. I bow still lower, and utter a string of courtesies. Dear heaven! If only I could put off the moment when our eyes must meet.

'Elder sister . . .'

The beloved voice! The most beloved voice on earth! I step forward, suddenly eager, but before I reach her *futon* my sister's gently-lifted hand stops me. I understand. My *imoto-san* doesn't want an emotional scene, and I give in to her wish. As I kneel on the *tatami* some distance away, we gaze at each other's faces. Hers is unchanged – as unchanged as her gentle voice. And her eyes are serene. *Too* serene? Too wholly calm?

Again my sister lifts her hand, and this time she points to the *fusuma* which leads to the next room. I am overcome with panic. So the – the *thing* is in there, in that gay little room which Ohatsu and Hiroo furnished for their heir-to-come, filling it with cuddly baby toys and lucky cranes. Must I see him – now? But Ohatsu shakes her head.

'Don't be frightened, *nei-san*. No one but me will ever see him,' she says. 'But there *is* something in there that I want you to look at. Then come back here, will you, elder sister? I'd like to speak to you – afterwards.'

Ah, our roles are reversed! Now small sister gives *me* orders, and I obey. What majestic personage has taken abode within Ohatsu's frail body? What forceful voice gives commands in Ohatsu's silken voice?

I tip-toe across the *tatami*, noiselessly open the sliding door, and my eyes go to the baby-carrier with its blue curtains. (Blue for a boy! Dear heaven!) The gaily-frilled curtains are tightly drawn, hiding entirely the – creature inside. I hear my own moan of relief. At that moment I catch sight of the portrait on Hiroo's easel.

Mà! It's a painting of Hiroo himself, a companion-piece to the one which I stood here admiring some weeks ago. In this painting, too, the young father is looking down at a bundle in his arms. But now his hair is white and his expression of horror tells of the utter loathsomeness of the object hidden in a shawl. The – monster. Ohatsu's monster! *Mà! Mà!* I hide my face in my hands, that feel like ice against my cheeks. Slowly I back away, reach blindly towards the *fusuma* of my sister's room.

'*Nei-san*, my husband painted that portrait during the night,' Ohatsu says. 'When he came out from that room at dawn – his hair had turned white.'

I kneel beside Ohatsu's *futon*. Between us conversation has become impossible. We two Hiroshima sisters have passed into a realm where words no longer have meaning. After a long silence, Ohatsu speaks.

'Elder sister, I have decided something. The cliff of Osima – I shall jump off it tomorrow evening, at sunset.'

I bow my head.

'Yes. It's so decided, deep within me. My baby and I will commit double suicide. I have two reasons.'

'Yes?'

'Hiroo must marry again and have normal children. He won't do that if I stay alive. You see, he loves me too much, *nei-san*.'

Ohatsu sends me a look that I have never seen in her eyes before. With passionate feeling she says,

'Every young man has a right to children, hasn't he? No man should have to fear that he'll one day hold a monster in his arms. Remember this in your own life, elder sister,' Ohatsu tells me, and as she speaks the words, she looks deep, deep into my eyes.

I want to cry out. With awful clarity I remember that August morning of the bomb, remember running towards the river through the black atomic rain that drenched us all to the skin. And every drop was as radio-active as the mushroom cloud itself! Domoto, as a scientist, may fear to say that radiation produces monsters. We survivors *know*!

It's with a great effort that I control my features, waiting for whatever more Ohatsu has to tell me.

'There's a second reason for what I'm going to do, elder sister.'

'Ah-h?'

'My suicide will be my gift to peace,' says Ohatsu. 'If my sacrifice becomes known, it may awaken women from their long sleep. They'll protest. For what happened to me may happen to many – one day.'

My little sister lies back on the *futon*. She's so wan, so white! A moment passes before she raises herself on her elbow.

'*Nei-san*, I have only one thing to give to life. It's my death.'

I draw in my breath. Dear heaven! And I who have always thought of small sister as 'weak'. Why, compared to her, mountains are but sandhills!

'Please leave me now,' Ohatsu whispers. '*Dozo*, elder sister. I am – a little tired.'

I try to get up. I stretch out my hand, and fumble for support. How will I find the strength to stand upright? I close my eyes. I bow my head. And it's then that I fall on the *tatami* in a dead faint.

II

'A LETTER for you, *oku-san*. Someone gave it to me at the bus stop at Kiosoko. An old servant . . .'

I take the message, thank the kindly bus passenger. On the pretty green envelope is Ohatsu's calligraphy, and my heart gives a leap. Has small sister thought better of yesterday's decision? Has she at least decided not to carry it out – today?

'Dear elder sister,' I read. 'Please come to Kiosoko this afternoon. At six o'clock Hiroo will be taking his honourable mother to the temple, so I'll be alone. I want you to help me dress in my best kimono. I'm not strong enough to tie the *obi* myself, nor to do my hair for the great occasion. Please come in a taxi. Please take me on to Osima. Obediently and lovingly,' she had ended. 'Small sister.'

Ohatsu's mistakes in writing make my eyes fill with tears. (How often haven't I scolded my little sister for her lop-sided calligraphy!) I control myself and pull open the bamboo gate. I've heard the sound of the noon bus and made a sudden decision. However painful, however difficult, I'll visit Kamei-san in Hondo-machi. After that I'll know how to act!

'Kiosoko?' the driver asks, for he remembers my usual destination. (How thoughtful of him.)

'No. A ticket to Hondo-machi. *Dozo.*'

I sink down in my seat. Oh, I dread my coming visit to this slum, where the poorest of our bomb survivors live! They're so scarred and mutilated that no one will give them work. It's lucky that foreign tourists never visit this shameful part of our city. Only a special errand would bring anyone to the hovels along the stinking river.

'Kamei-san's house? At the end of the alley,' answers an old man whose eyes have no lids. He peers at me from under lumpy keloid scars. 'But she won't let anyone inside her shack. You'd better turn back,' he says harshly.

I shake my head and hurry on, leaning against the wind from the river. Oh dear! Kamei-san's abode can scarcely be called even a shack. The walls are made of boards and bits of sheet metal. Its 'door' is a sack nailed to the rotted wood. And the hunched-up woman outside looks just as battered as her hut.

'May I come in, *oku-san?*'

'*Nie!*'

Kamei-san's 'no' is like a slap in the face – in the face of the whole world. Is it possible that this ashen-faced creature was once lovely Kamei-san, who owned a flower shop in my mama-san's street? If only I could have turned and run away!

'I'm Yuka Nakamura,' I say, embarrassed. 'The sister of – Ohatsu Shimitzu.'

'*Mà!*'

So it's all over Hiroshima already! Kamei-san's eyes widen in pity, and I understand that the news of Ohatsu's – monster has spread like wildfire among the ever-frightened survivors. (Ah, the atom bomb's never done with, never done with, as Sam said. It will go on for ever.) Kamei-san gently puts her hand on my arm. Now she knows why I have come!

'I can't ask you inside, my poor Nakamura-san. You see, I've never allowed anyone to look at . . .'

I take a step backward. I smother a scream. For a sudden gust from the river has lifted the sacking, and I catch sight on the floor of a faceless object that stares at me with eyes that express all the agony of the world. They don't focus properly, yet seem to accuse me just because I belong to the species responsible for this creature's unutterable woe.

'Poor *oku-san*! I wish you hadn't seen her. Perhaps fate willed you to see her – and to understand.'

Long years of grief have worn out Kamei-san. She leans her tired back against the wall of her hut.

'Nakamura-san, everyone knows my story. I was five months on the way when the annihilation plane flew over Hiroshima. Three months later my child was born, one of many monsters produced by women who were pregnant at the time of the blast. Few of the others lived more than days, but new monsters have been born – many more than are noted in the records. They too, most fortunately, died at birth for the most part.'

She's looking at me so strangely. I feel that Kamei-san wants to say something more, and I dread her words. I have guessed what they will be.

'Your little sister,' she murmurs, 'may she find strength to do what *I* should have done. You must describe my monster-child to her. Yes, yes.'

We quickly say good-bye to each other. Gathering all my strength, I throw a second look at her shack, but the merciful wind has slackened. The sack has again become a door. I bow to Kamei-san, then bow again to the suffering object I cannot see. I flee . . .

* * *

'Is it you, *nei-san*?'

It's small sister's voice. So she's already up? I beg the young taxi-driver to wait, and slide open the *shojii*. Ohatsu is standing fully dressed in the dimly-lit room.

'I am ready,' she says.

'But *imoto-san*, I thought that I was going to help you do your hair?'

Then I see that my sister, though still weak from childbirth, has managed to do her hair most elaborately. She's tied the difficult *obi* herself. Yes, Ohatsu's – all prepared! A flat package leans against the *fusuma*, and a basket with her potted plants stands beside the baby-carrier. Its frilled curtains are so tightly drawn that nothing shows. (Oh, thank heaven for that. Thank heaven!) In her enchanting voice Ohatsu gives me instructions.

'Elder sister, in this parcel is Hiroo's self-portrait that you saw yesterday. I want you to exhibit it. You must tell people why my husband's hair turned white in one night.'

(Oh, small sister awes me! Such spirit, such style! Usually as timid as a moth, she seems to have undergone a vast transformation. Gently but firmly Ohatsu-san gives me further instructions.)

'Ask Michiko to take care of my plants.' There's a look of almost too-deep understanding in small sister's eyes as she gazes at the flowering plants. 'It took thousands of years for each species of flower to reach its present perfection, *nei-san*. But in a few moments' time all plant life on earth may be destroyed for ever.'

Ohatsu clasps her hands in a gesture of pleading. It's her loveliest gesture. Looking into my eyes, she cries,

'Beg the destroyers not to ruin in *one minute* all of our earth's beauty! Promise me that you'll do that, elder sister. Promise me!'

'I promise.'

'Then – let us go,' whispers Ohatsu.

'I will follow you, small sister.'

It's unimaginable, of course, that a younger sister shall precede her senior. But Ohatsu understands that she has suddenly become a person of great stature. Lifting her baby-carrier by its plastic handles, she lightly steps through the open *shojii* and gets into the taxi.

'To – Osima!'

(Oh, no! Not that, not that!)

'Please, driver-san, stop on the beach road beside Osima cliff,' Ohatsu tells the driver, giving him her gentle smile.

She has managed to speak so calmly that I stare at her, overcome. The great self-control that Ohatsu has imposed on herself since the moment she saw her monster-infant helps her to act as if this were an ordinary day. With calm eyes she watches the country-side slip past – the rice-paddies, the sunny little gardens. Not a muscle moves in her face when the famous suicide cliff looms up before us. A sea-gull on the summit lifts its wings as we get close, then takes off for the sea.

The taxi stops and we step out. It's small sister, not I, who pays the fare. So as to gaze at her dazzling beauty a moment longer, the young man tries to chat.

'You're taking your baby to the sea, *oku-san*,' he asks.

'To the sea? Yes, yes, to the – sea,' Ohatsu answers. 'Come, *nei-san*,' she murmurs.

We hurry along the path leading to the cliff, which is shaped much like a sugar loaf. Ohatsu walks quickly, perhaps because the sun is about to set. At the foot of the pine-covered cliff she stops.

'We must say good-bye here, *nei-san*. I must climb my cliff – alone.'

I break down then and beg Ohatsu to let me go with her. I feel that I don't wish to live without beloved small sister. I'll accompany her to the summit of the cliff – and beyond.

'Small sister. I'm coming with you . . . all the way!'

'*No.*' Ohatsu's voice is a whisper, but it has the power of a command. 'No. You must live, *nei-san*!' She gazes at me, and her eyes have an almost pitying look. 'It's *you* who will tell people why I had to die. It's you who will fight for a peaceful world. If my sacrifice is to be of use – then you must live, elder sister.'

I bow my head. Small sister has given her last order. It would be a sin to disobey.

'I shall leave you now, *nei-san*,' Ohatsu says. 'It will only take a few minutes. Wait here. Soon you will see my face in the setting sun,' she promises me. 'It will shine from there for ever – to give you courage to fight.'

My sister picks up the blue baby-carrier which she had set down while we talked. She straightens her thin little-girl's back.

'Good-bye, elder sister. Thank you for not trying to stop me. I've always counted on you. I knew that I could keep counting on you – to the last minute of my life.'

Small sister's serenity and inner nobility fill me with pride. I follow her example. Without weeping, we go through the required gestures of saying farewell, bowing low, calmly smiling and thanking each other for past happiness. Then Ohatsu turns and takes the path up the cliff. Knowing that she won't turn for a last look, I have to fight down a scream. Ohatsu! Stop! My darling!

I follow her with my eyes. As my sister nears the top of her pine-sprinkled mountain – the handles of her baby-carrier clutched in her hand – she begins to move as swiftly as a wind-blown leaf. I hold my breath. Awed, I watch her, a simple Japanese girl, setting out on a great mission. So young, brave and ardent, small sister has wrenched herself from personal happiness to fulfil the fate towards which she's been moving ever since August sixth, nineteen forty-five. Ah-h! Suddenly I know that her sacrifice will not have been in vain. People will understand! For war, like that poor creature in the basket, is a brainless monster which cannot be allowed to survive.

Now!

The sun is sinking. It is approaching the rim of the sea. I drop to my knees on the beach, and as I lift my face to the sun, I give a gasp of joy. My sister's face *does* smile down at me from the centre of that burning flower. I gaze at her features, and their perfection is such that I stretch my arms towards her in adoration.

'Small sister!'

Ah, forgive me, Ohatsu! Forgive my lament, my one shout of pain. The mountain echoes my word 'sister' and I let myself slump on to the sand. No, I haven't acquired my frail sister's iron strength yet. I'm so sorry.

But night comes soon to hide my weakness and my tears with its dark blanket. I hear the echo from the mountain as blackness covers the Inland Sea. Sister – sister . . .

12

'Look, Mama-san! There's a thousand people by Uncle Hiroo's gate. More than a thousand! A hundred.'

'Are there, *dakko-chan*?' I say, for I wouldn't like to correct my little son. How should a small boy know about numbers? Besides, isn't it a good thing that my children are impressed by the many people come to pay their respects to small sister? I did right to bring them along with me against Aunt Matsui's advice. The nephew and niece of a great heroine are heirs to a fortune. Oh yes, Ohatsu has left Michiko and *dakko-chan* far more than her beloved plants.

'*Gomen kudasai. Dozo.*'

Mà! But what's happened to the face of Hiroo's mother? It looks as contorted as her son's. And the aged *genan*, who stands by their side before the open coffin, has shrunk together. After greeting me in his old-fashioned manner, he carefully arranges my white roses at the coffin's head. Then we exchange a look.

'Take the children, please,' I whisper to him.

It's as I let go of their warm paws that my boy slides his little plush pigeon into my hand. All right, then! I promised my son to let his favourite toy keep Ohatsu 'company' and I can't go back on my word. (I'll slip the peace dove with its red glass eyes into the coffin when none of the Shimitzus are watching. What harm can that do?)

They're all here! The whole family has gathered, and are crowding the dim room. I'm amazed at the change in Hiroo's honourable relatives, who used so to awe Ohatsu and me. Why, they look – quite ordinary. Insignificant! Then I understand. It's Ohatsu's great personality that dwarfs them. In the light of two candles, small sister lies there humbly. But she dominates the room.

'Yuka . . .'

It's Sam-san! In the crowd I hadn't seen him before. Dear Sam! In honour of the occasion he's put on a tie and he's slicked down his unruly hair. These efforts of my betrothed at tidiness bring the tears to my eyes. Oh, he looks just like an overgrown boy, in his shrunken seersucker suit! Among the kimono-clad Shimitzu men Sam seems very much an alien. An – *alien?* Sam? The look he sends me shows his understanding of the abyss of my grief. No, Sam's no alien! Has anyone so identified himself with suffering Hiroshima as my darling Sam?

Hiroo steps forward. Oh dear! His hair's exactly the colour of his white kimono of mourning.

'Honourable ancestors!' he murmurs, after bowing to the photographs above Ohatsu's coffin.

How quiet the room is! No one breathes while Hiroo dips his fingers in the purified water, then lifts the veil that covers small sister's face. Ah-h! There's a gasp. The whole Shimitzu family seems overcome by the physical beauty of the girl whose moral beauty has already staggered them. The hush is deep as Hiroo wets her lips and turns to the photographs of his ancestors. He bows his head.

'My wife is on her way, *hotoke-sans*. She won't be long now,' he tells the venerable photographs.

Hiroo falters. Then he controls himself and asks his ancestors to forgive him for having brought disaster to their line.

'You must also forgive me for not continuing my branch, honoured *hotokes*. I cannot re-marry! I cannot give you successors. Indeed, I am more dead than my young wife who sacrificed her personal happiness and her life to warn mankind of the radiation peril hanging over generations still to come. Forgive me, honourable ancestors! Tomorrow I am entering a Buddhist monastery.'

Mà! My hands have broken my fan in two. The splintered bamboo cuts into my clenched fingers.

'Ancestors,' says Hiroo. '*Dozo*. Listen to what I must say. It is rumoured that one of the plane crew that atom-bombed Hiroshima locked himself in a Christian monastery to expiate his deed. I can never expiate mine! I forced my wife, irradiated by that bomb, to bear a child. It was a heinous crime. But I did it for your sake, honoured family. Those bombers and I – we murdered Ohatsu.'

I hear a sob. It's Hiroo's mother, but as swiftly as

her son, she recovers her samurai-dignity and stands at attention beneath the line of ancestors.

And now it's my turn to say good-bye to personal happiness. My Japanese words Sam will not understand, but the gist of them he will know, for I have told him in a letter.

'Small sister . . .' (Oh, what's happened to my voice? It stays in my throat and only a whisper slips out.) 'Small sister,' I say, and touch her lips with water, 'I asked your permission to follow you in death, but you said it was my solemn duty to remain alive. You said that I should tell people how and why you died. Now I dedicate myself to that sacred task.'

Oh, what big words for someone like *me* to pronounce! Solemn duty? Sacred task? But the three of us, Ohatsu, Hiroo and I, are such small, simple people. Because of the great events in today's world, we have been called upon to act like *great* people. We have all made that total sacrifice which Maeda said was demanded for the sake of peace.

'Small sister,' I say, gathering my strength for the ordeal. 'I promised also to obey another wish of yours. I shall never marry! I, too, was touched by the bomb, and I will not risk cursing any man with tainted offspring. This is my second vow. Hear me, *imoto-san*!' I cry, but my glance travels over the faces to meet Sam's stricken eyes.

I sway. Instantly Maeda's hand grips my elbow. Ah! My *sensi*'s hand will always be there to support me –

that's the one consoling thought on this fearful day. I draw myself upright. No! Small sister walked unsupported up the suicide cliff of Osima. I, too, must never depend on sustaining hands, only on the strength of my inner core – like my little sister. I take a step forward! I stand alone.

But, what's this? Sam has gone up to Ohatsu's coffin, and although I beg him silently not to speak before this group of grieving Hiroshimans, I see him open his lips. Oh, Sam's perspiring! His forehead is damp as he stands looking down at the young girl in her coffin, the girl whose death was indirectly caused by the same bomb that killed scores of thousands before her.

His lips move. Poor Sam! My poor darling! He's like a man on the torture rack, and only after a long struggle can he force out one word. But it's the most difficult of all words to utter.

'Forgive!' says Sam. 'Forgive!'

At that great moment I hear cars drawing up outside and the old *genan* tells us that it is time to leave for the crematorium. Everyone tumbles out for air and for a glass of saké under the shady cypresses. Dazedly I take my place in a car . . .

Boom! Boom! Ah, can it be that a whole hour's gone by in this ugly crematorium in downtown Hiroshima? How long it takes to burn up a young girl! One would think that her slender body would be consumed in a flash, but an eternity passes as we kneel, waiting, in the adjoining room. Strange! It took only a second to incinerate our town, causing a hundred thousand tragedies whose end is not in sight. Can it be that it's easier to destroy a whole city than to eradicate the final consequences of the crime?

Ah! Now – at last.

All that's left of small sister – a bowlful of tiny bones and ashes – is carried in. The time has come for the last ceremony. Hiroo and I get to our feet, then kneel again on the *tatami*, taking a chopstick each. (How stiflingly hot it is! My kimono sticks to my skin.) Manipulating our two chopsticks together, we pick up Ohatsu's charred bones and put them in a lacquered box that will stand in the Shimitzu family's ancestral cabinet.

No, no, I can't go on! I shake too much. I keep dropping small sister's bones. Ah, but that's not a bone – that small red object among the ashes! *Mà!* Isn't it a glass eye from *dakko-chan's* peace dove? I gasp. *Dakko-chan!* My little son! Oh, I *must* go on for your sake – for the sake of that innocent world for which Ohatsu gave her life.

The thought gives me strength. It steels my will. How am I to carry out my task of fighting for a peaceful world if I can't lift small sister's bones, which are as light as snow-flakes – and as white?

Chopstick, I beg. Help me carry out my ordeal. *Dozo.* Help me, chopstick, brave chopstick.

GLOSSARY OF JAPANESE WORDS

Anata: term of appelation between spouses
Arrigato gosaimas: thank you very much
Ashitori: leg clutch used in Japanese-style wrestling
Butsudan: family altar
Buyens: Japanese ornamental hairpins
Dakko-chan: 'Cuddly one'
Furoji: orphans
"*Fu-ro-sa-to de, Ma-to aō*": "Let me see my native
   town again"
Furoshiki: kerchief in which objects can be wrapped
Fusuma: inner sliding panel
Futon: Japanese-style bed
Gembaku no hana: The flower of the atom bomb
Genan: old family retainer
Getas: wooden sandals
Giri-gift: 'keep-sweet-relationship gift'
'*Gomen kudasai. Dozo.*': 'Excuse me, please.'
Gumi: gang
Hà: exclamation of surprise or wonder
Haiku: short Japanese poem
Haro-san: slang for 'an American'
Homongi: party kimono, 'visiting kimono'
Hotoke: ancestral spirit
Imoto-san: younger sister
Kyoju: professor
'*Komban wa*': 'Good evening. Hello!'

Mà! : exclamation
'Moshi-moshi!' : 'Hello-hello!' (telephone)
Mushi : insect
Nakano : matchmaker
Nei-san : elder sister
Obi : Japanese sash
Oku-san : madame
Ori-tsuru : lucky cranes
Oshiva-san : 'pusher' (on trains and subways)
Pikadon : Japanese expression for atom bomb. Literally: flash-bang
Roka : wooden veranda
Sà! : exclamation of annoyance
Saké : Japanese rice wine
Sensi : master
Shojü : sliding door
Suchi : raw fish
Sumo : Japanese wrestling
Tabis : Japanese socks
Tanka : Japanese poem
Tatami : Japanese straw mats
Tsukimi : – party: Moon-viewing party
Yoku irashai mashita : you are welcome
Yome : daughter-in-law, 'bride of the house'
Yubikiti-promise: promise that cannot be broken
Yukata : cotton kimono
Yuraku-cho de aimasho : song. 'Meet me at Yuraku-cho station'
Zori : straw sandals